ROBERT JAMES (R J) MITCHELL was brought up in Stirling and from an early age developed a keen interest in history, especially medieval history. He graduated from Glasgow University with MA Honours in British, European and Scottish Medieval History, and joined Strathclyde Police in 1989.

Mitchell was initially detailed beat duties out of the former Blackhill Police Office and then Baird Street Police Office in the former 'D' Division, and still cherishes his first set of shoulder numerals which were D325. A keen squash player, Mitchell captained the West of Scotland squash team and has played competitively at national level.

After 12 years of service, RJ decided to concentrate on full-time writing and so resigned from Strathclyde Police. He had already started to enjoy an increasingly successful career as a freelance sports journalist under the name of Bob James, and his coups included exclusive interviews with boxers Mike Tyson and Lennox Lewis.

It was while recovering from an appendicitis that RJ decided to write his first book *Parallel Lines: The Glasgow Supremacy*, a crime thriller set in Glasgow, and which drew heavily on his own police experiences. His second book – *The Hurting: The Glasgow Terror* – followed in 2012, which was nominated for The People's Book Prize. In November 2013, *The Longest Shadow,* the third book in the DS Thoroughgood series, was published to critical acclaim and RJ Mitchell's fourth book – *The Shift* – was runner-up in the final of the 2017 People's Book Prize.

The Shadow of Fear

First published in 2018 by
Nine Elms Books
Unit 6B
Clapham North Arts Centre
26–32 Voltaire Road
London SW4 6DH
Email: inquiries@bene-factum.co.uk
www.bene-factum.co.uk

ISBN: 978-1-910533-33-8
Epub: 978-1-910533-34-5

Cover design: Tony Hannaford
Book design: Dominic Horsfall

Set in Borgia Pro
Printed in the UK

Acknowledgements

FIRSTLY, thanks, to you, the reader, whoever you may be, for without you there would be no point.

As always, thanks to my darling wife Arlene, a lady who has the patience of a saint and has needed every ounce of it!

Grateful thanks to my literary agent Susan 'Suzy-Q' Mears for helping secure the deal that helped Ludovic Fear escape from my mind.

To Anthony Weldon for seeing the potential in Ludovic Fear and adding *The Shadow of Fear* to his stable at Nine Elms Books while also being consistently patient and accessible to an author who can prove demanding...on occasions!

To Mike French for his hard work on the edit of what I hope will be the first of a few collaborations!

Also sincere gratitude is due to my old 'colleague' Les Trueman for providing an excellent sounding-board and a fine expert reader.

Big thanks to David Hunter and Craig Sinclair of WH Smith in co-ordinating the monster Scottish signing tour that will accompany myself and the bold Ludovic over the weeks and months of 2018 ahead of us.

Finally, if I've forgotten anyone, please accept my sincerest apologies.

As the late, great, Dave Allen once said: "Good night and may your god go with you!" Enjoy!

1

THE air was filled with raucous howls and expletive-laced shouting, punctuated by the rasping of metal on metal as tin cups were scraped and then rattled against the fencing that boxed in the first floor of HMP Barlinnie's notorious 'C Hall'.

When the iron safety door at the top end of the hall was slammed shut and the click of the turning lever confirmed that the last screw had left the building, the inmates knew that the only law that now prevailed was that of the jungle and its ruler.

At the far end of the first floor a hulking, unshaven inmate in a red shirt tenderly set down an ornate mahogany Victorian rocking chair, a symbol of the power wielded by the villain who was cock of the dung-heap filled by the dregs of those who had fallen foul of the Scottish Criminal Justice System. His unquestioned dominance of the 'Big Hoose', as it was colloquially known, was once again about to be underlined.

As visceral cheers filled the building, the metallic echoes were replaced by the chanting of one word: "Grass," as the inmates made sure that the man who was about to pay for his transgressions against his fellow convicts could expect no mercy.

For this was the domain of a half-burned fiend, known simply as Jamieson to all who had no choice but to adhere to the barbaric rule he had established by greasing the palms of underpaid prison warders and surrounding himself with a set of henchmen who knew they would be taken care of on the outside if they looked after their master on the inside. His reign within the prison operated outside the normal rules of society and was unchallenged.

A stocky figure slipped out from behind a white cell door to the right of the beautifully carved rocking chair and eased onto the seat.

Jamieson's features had been hideously scarred in an acid attack by a gangland rival, and this, along with his snow-white, straggling shoulder-length hair, gave Jamieson a unique and ghoulish appearance.

He swept the assembled gathering with a piercingly shrewd gaze, before his right hand suddenly shot up to signal immediate silence.

He spoke, in understated, measured tones that still failed to eradicate the roughness of his grating Glaswegian accent oozing assured menace: "Bring him forward."

From the opposite side of the landing a struggling figure, restrained by the cast-iron grip of two more red-shirted man-mountains, his prison boots scraping across the meshed hall flooring, was dragged towards the almost uninterested crime king, reclining in his chair.

Impassive, Jamieson sat gently massaging the white-streaked ginger goatee that gave him the almost feral appearance of a big cat assessing its next prey.

As the struggling victim was slammed onto his knees in front of the throne, his head shot up, revealing youthful features stained with stress and hollowed eyes rimmed red by fear of the ordeal that he was about to undergo.

"Please, Jamieson, I begs you, it's aw been a misunder-standin'. I did 'ne know Johnny Whelan was supplying yous with the smack, if I did I wid never hae opened ma mooth but…" Before he could finish his plea bargaining, Jamieson jumped to his feet and smashed a steel toecap into the young criminal's guts, who toppled over clutching his midriff as he gasped for air.

"Shut the fuck up, McCallum, you grass," said Jamieson and once more the air filled with a vicious cheering that expressed the bloodlust that was coursing through the veins of every member of the crowd of revenge-thirsty inmates.

Every resident, that was, except one seemingly detached figure at the opposite end of the first floor of C Hall, whose face was now being scanned by Jamieson for any sign of a reaction to the unfolding events he was orchestrating with such calculated insouciance.

The onlooker showed no sign of any emotion, exuding a studied indifference to the kangaroo court and its hapless victim's likely punishment.

Yet his cornflower-blue eyes locked and held Jamieson's unflinchingly.

As the inmates continued to chorus their vicious desires for McCallum's impending fate, the crime lord's goatee twitched, and an immaculate set of teeth, punctuated by two symmetrical gold crowns, lit up his scarred face.

He held up his hand and again the chanting died away: "Prepare the chicken for the spit," spat Jamieson, with another searching glance at the watcher with the impenetrable eyes.

McCallum was dragged back onto his feet and, despite his desperate protestations, rammed against the metallic fencing of the first floor gantry. One of Jamieson's minions snapped his feet apart while the other slapped his two hands onto the peeling, white painted railing above the enclosure.

Then a third inmate, an old scar flushed with feral anticipation, stepped forward and in one brutal motion ripped both the prison fatigue trousers and the boxers below them down around McCallum's ankles.

"For fuck's sake naw, dinne dae me, Jamieson, it wiz a mistake I promise yous," pleaded the helpless victim, even as his wrists were quickly bound tight with black insulating tape.

"Burn him," spat the Bar-L's unofficial ruler, and the inmates went berserk, repeating his words over and over again in throaty delirium.

The man with the scar needed no second invitation.

Pulling a toilet roll out of the left pocket of his fatigue jacket he ripped a strip ten sheets long and, turning to his two confederates, shouted: "Spread him."

With Jamieson's two hulking enforcers holding him tight, all of McCallum's frantic struggling counted for nought. Nevertheless, he continued to beg desperately for clemency from the crime lord.

"Naw, naw, naw please gie me another chance, Jamieson," he grovelled, but to no avail.

McCallum's feet were stretched to an angle of almost 120 degrees, and Scarface inserted the toilet roll, coated in sparkling expectorant, up his rectum until only a trail of five sheets dangled down. The victim's red prison shirt had been ripped from his torso, leaving McCallum naked bar the trousers now around his ankles.

Turning to his ruler for the final order, Scarface was given the curt two-word instruction: "Light it."

From his right fist appeared an orange plastic lighter, and Scarface instantly snapped it into flame, then theatrically held it aloft for a moment while the crowd howled: "Torch him, torch him," until Jamieson's right hand, its index finger projecting outwards, slowly rose above his head and a menacing silence fell once more.

Then, dramatically, he dropped his arm, and Scarface applied the light, making sure the flame had taken hold.

"Naw, naw, for fuck's sake..." McCallum screamed as he was hurled round by his burly minders and then propelled down the gangway to run the gauntlet of cruel, glinting iron bars, sharpened wooden stakes and any other form of weapon that the inmates had been able to get their hands on.

For now the ordeal known to all and sundry within HMP Barlinnie as 'The Chicken Run' had truly begun. McCallum had to negotiate the 200 yards of the top floor of C Hall, enduring the blows of the vengeful inmates lining the gangway, before the burning toilet roll's flames reached his skin and scorched their lethal route into his defenceless insides.

Felled by a vicious blow administered by a wooden chair leg, he struggled to get up. Stumbling onto all fours, McCallum's nostrils filled with the smell of burning paper that he knew would soon be replaced with that of barbecued flesh. He looked imploringly into the faces of those inmates lining his descent to hell and begged for mercy: "Help us, help us, for the luv o' Mother Mary," he screamed.

His pleading was met with a mouthful of green phlegm that slid down his tear-stained face. Onwards he lurched, half-crawling, before he raised himself once again onto unsteady feet and attempted to stumble into some kind of a sprint.

As he did so the glint of metal caught his eye, and he ducked under the descending bar, which missed his cheek by an inch. The breeze of the backdraft momentarily refreshed him.

McCallum quickly refocused his gaze on the far end of the Chicken Run, where stood the bucket of water that was the one hope of salvation, but which still seemed a long way off.

As he flailed on, he failed to spot the outstretched brush handle that lay in wait to trip him, and he landed face first with a vicious thwack on the mesh floor. It was then that McCallum started to feel the flames sear his skin. His howl of pain was drowned by the banshee chorus of the inmates ranting for his blood.

On and on he stumbled, his bound hands raised to ward off the rain of blows that battered him. Only 50 yards remained, yet the end of the Chicken Run might as well have been on the dark side of the moon for all the hope McCallum had of reaching it.

The beating continued unremittingly. As he pushed himself onwards, his legs shaking, McCallum was grabbed by the hair and his head rammed into the side fencing before he was propelled forward again, blood streaming from his forehead and his vision blurred from the onset of concussion.

"Help me, help me," he begged in a bloody gurgle, to no one in particular, all hope drained from his voice.

His pleas for mercy fell on deaf ears, and the faint hope drained from his voice.

Then, just as it seemed everything was lost, a powerful figure strode out from the far side of the mesh-enclosed gantry, and the attention of the captive crowd diverted from McCallum's pitiful writhing and agonised whimpers to the unexpected arrival on centre stage.

To the amazement of the inmates the man with the corn-flower-blue eyes strode forward, holding a fire extinguisher. This unforeseen development brought a descending hush on the gathering that had not seemed remotely conceivable moments before.

In front of the almost silent audience he began to spray the whimpering McCallum with the contents of the extinguisher, turning the tortured inmate snow-white in a blizzard of foam, as he stumbled back onto his knees. His rescuer pulled McCallum to his feet: "Get up and start walking… fast," he said in an emotionless voice.

They had not gone ten yards when, the element of surprise gone, the two brutes who had originally brought McCallum forward to face his punishment at the feet of Jamieson charged down the gangway after them.

The sound of their feet chinking on the steel mesh was all the warning that McCallum's unexpected guardian angel needed: "On you go," he said, pushing the youth forwards and turning to face his persecutors.

The inmates found their voice again: they bayed for blood. "Dae him, dae him," they howled in rage. The taller of the two henchmen sprinted forward, intending to be the first to wreak revenge on the figure who had dared to thwart Jamieson's authority.

Five yards away from McCallum's saviour he spat out: "I'm gonna slice and dice ye, Fear…like a packet o' square sausage." From the waistband of his fatigues he whipped out a butcher's cleaver that glinted with cruel beauty.

Raising it above his head, he advanced and swung it downwards with everything he had. His target ducked inside the lethal arc and smashed his right hand into his attacker's ribs, before twisting violently and wrapping his two hands around the knifeman's wrist, in one precise movement throwing him over his back and slamming him down on the gantry's mesh, the cleaver slipping off the flooring and dropping over the side of the gangway and onto the concrete of C Hall's ground floor 50 feet below.

Fear hammered his right fist into the convict's ruddy features in three sharp blows that rendered him unconscious just as the second of the two pursuers closed for combat.

Rolling free, Fear used his escape move to ram straight into the second inmate's feet and, still on his back, aimed a brutal kick upwards into the man's groin, which doubled him up in agony.

Fear leapt up, grabbed the staggering henchman by his hair and smashed his face off his right knee. He immediately went limp and dropped like a stone onto the mesh floor.

Slowly Fear backed away towards the far end of the gangway where McCallum was now seated on the bucket of water whimpering with relief.

"Whit the fuck did ye go and dae that for?" the youth ungratefully demanded. Before his saviour could answer, his gaze was diverted to Jamieson's impending arrival, escorted by three more of his underlings.

"Fucked if I know the answer to that one, amigo," replied Ludovic Fear, surveying the approaching group and weighing up the odds against him. They were too great, he realised, but balling his fists he assumed a defensive position, signalling to Jamieson and his heavies that he was determined to fight to the last.

The crime lord pushed silently through his guards, who Fear observed were armed menacingly with a baseball bat, cudgel and another glinting machete.

Standing three feet away from him, Jamieson let the silence that had descended on the watching crowd hang unbearably. Finally, he spoke:

"At last I have a reaction from you, Fear – and I'll gie you this, it wiz an impressive demo o' your expertise. You and I needs to speak, but first I'm afraid that your foolish young freend still has a price to pay for his stupidity. This time I'd be grateful if you stayed out o' my business, however noble yer sentiments maybees."

The game was up. Fear saw that further resistance would be futile.

Turning towards McCallum, he shrugged his shoulders. "I'm sorry, son. But at least I saved your arse."

Jamieson gave a short laugh. "If you heads back along tae ma cell, we'll talk there, after the kid pays his price and we decide whit yours is."

Fear nodded curtly, and as he stepped past one of Jamieson's underlings the granite-jawed hood nudged his shoulder. "You and me sometime soon, soldier boy."

Behind Fear's impenetrable features rage surged, and before the cruel smile on the thug's face had faded he rammed his right elbow across his throat and grabbed his tormentor's testicles with his left hand.

"Enjoy, fucker!" spat Fear and applied pressure.

"Bastard," hissed the hood, his eyes popping, before Fear stepped back and smashed a right hand to the solar plexus that dropped his shrieking tormentor on the floor, writhing in agony.

Fear strode on.

For a moment the only sound was the piteous groaning of the prostrate hood, but soon abuse started to fill the air, and a hail of tin beakers began to rain down on Fear. Jaw set, he pulled back his shoulders, kept his head up and walked at a steady pace towards Jamieson's cell.

What was about to happen next was anyone's guess, but turning to face the mob from the cell's open doorway Ludovic Fear spat three defiant words: "Qui audet adipiscitur," not caring how few of his listeners would know that was the Latin motto of the SAS: "Who dares wins".

2

As he waited for his audience with Jamieson, Fear could hear the change in the tone of the din now filling C Hall. With the distraction removed, the inmates could return to the main business. An expectant silence fell. It was shattered by McCallum's final tortured scream, and then a bloodcurdling cheer broke like a giant wave. Fear was left in no doubt that the snitch had paid the ultimate price for his treachery. He felt a pang of sympathy. But it was now his turn to face Jamieson.

The noise of leather slapping on the steel-mesh flooring of the gantry grew louder and louder. Jamieson was coming.

Fear scanned the cell from its bunk beds to the writing desk, the TV sitting comfortably on top another sign of the privileged position Jamieson occupied as C Hall's de facto ruler, and saw there was precious little that could be utilised for purposes of self-defence.

When Jamieson reached the doorway of his cell he hovered for a moment and swept the former soldier with shrewd emerald eyes before smiling thinly at his guest: "Sit doon why don't you, big man," he suggested amicably and gestured towards the red plastic chair parked under the desk.

Fear pulled the chair out, turned it to face Jamieson, then lowered himself into it, all the time keeping his eyes trained on his host and the tooled-up henchmen by his side. They parted briefly for the rocking chair throne to be brought back into the cell, and its owner sat down before waving his left hand dismissively to his attendants. "Awright boys, you can leave us noo, shut the door behind you."

The civility was a surprise and left Fear trying to predict just where the next few minutes were going to take him.

Jamieson smiled and then quickly pulled out a tin of Golden Virginia tobacco and a packet of Rizlas and began to roll a cigarette. He said nothing, but his eyes lifted as though to gauge the effect on his visitor. When the cigarette was ready, he leant forward and passed it across. Fear took it, trying not to show his surprise at this manoeuvre.

Jamieson deftly repeated the process, then whipped out a shining Zippo lighter and lit both cigarettes. Though deeply suspicious, Fear was grateful for this brief pause before Jamieson told him his fate.

Inhaling deeply and then expelling the smoke in a series of smoke-rings, the master criminal gave Fear a piercing look and began to speak.

"Yer life is a fuckin' mess considering how many medals you won, soldier boy?" he opened with a sentence that invited an answer.

Ludovic Fear met his darting eyes but said nothing.

"So tell me how does a Browning 9mm Pistol and 33 rounds of ammo find its way into your bedside cabinet without you havin' a bleedin' Scooby aboot it?" asked Jamieson, locking onto his visitor's impassive features

Fear took another drag and exhaled slowly before replying: "Anything is possible when you're fitted up, Jamieson. You of all people should know that."

"The problem is that for me and ma sort that's an occupational hazard, Fear. But for a decorated hero of the SAS with a chest full of shiny bawbees, who goes and gets himself court-marshalled and then found guilty in the civilian courts, it's an absolute fuckin' tragedy. Capiche?" said Jamieson, summing up Fear's situation before adding with cruel relish: "Bottom line is that your life is in ruins, you've nowhere to fuckin' go and apart from hirin' your gun out, hombre, whit kind of work is oot there for you?"

Jamieson held his gaze, scratching the right side of his ruined face with a long and neatly manicured fingernail.

Attempting to force home his point and underline just how bleak Fear's situation was, Jamieson warmed to his task: "Once upon a time you wiz the man, feared by the RA Provos – and no fuckin' wonder given what you got up tae in the Province. Then there was the joab you did on the Taliban and the rest o' these mad motherfuckin' Arabs, but now yous just a common baw-bag o' a villain like the rest o' us animals in the Big Hoose…the one big difference being you have expertise that a freend o' mine needs, pal," and there Jamieson left the carrot to dangle.

His temper rising, Fear couldn't help his jaw setting again, but he kept himself in check and took an inward breath before smiling and replying evenly: "There's big money to be made on 'The Circuit' and I'm not exactly short of ex-colleagues from The Regiment who are fillin' their boots in all four corners of the globe, so if it's all the same to your 'freend', I'll do my time and see where I go from there, Jamieson."

Their eyes met and held, like two poker players trying to read each other. As things stood, Jamieson seemed to have all the cards. How long would it take him to bring up his futile intervention in the summary justice that had now clearly been meted out to McCallum?

"That's as maybe; but what if I had something a damn sight less risky and maybees more lucrative that might set you up for any life you want to build and help you forget about the shaftin' you just had from the very people you been riskin' your life tae protect?" asked Jamieson amicably.

Fear shook his head and snapped: "Just how is going to work for the biggest crim in Bar-L gonna help me out, Jamieson? The only thing that's gonna do is make my life 100 times worse, if that's possible."

Leaning forward in his rocking chair Jamieson patted his visitor on the back of his right hand. Fear withdrew it, tightening it into a fist.

Almost in a whisper Jamieson soothed: "Now dinne be daein' anything else ye may live, or may naw live, tae regret and just listen to me, soldier boy. I been watching you for a while noo, wondering just what was going to push yer buttons and make you do somethin' stupid and thankfully wee McCallum's Chicken Run proved just whit the doc ordered and you obliged, big time. Bottom line is you just canne let a lost cause go, can ye, hombre?"

Jamieson kept his eyes locked on Fear's, pushing himself soothingly to and fro in his rocking chair, a thin smile of self-satisfaction playing over his scarred lips. He held all the aces and wanted Fear to know it.

Sighing almost as if it pained him to be the bearer of bad news, Jamieson leaned back in his chair and continued: "The big problem for you, Sergeant Ludovic Fear, is that it was'ne me that wee shit McCallum grassed up; it was somebody far nastier. Somebody who you really dinne wanna be crossing, but somebody who is prepared to let your bad judgement slide, if you are prepared to help lend him yer expertise for a special joab, which, I hastens to add, hombre, you will be quids-in for, big time. So whit I'm doin' here is actin' as yer guid Samaritan and givin' you a get-out of-jail-free card aw in wan, so tae speak," and at that Jamieson cuffed his right palm of his left knee before dissolving into peals of laughter at his own joke.

Fear jumped to his feet, his patience with this game of verbal cat and mouse now done: "Like I told you before, I ain't interested."

"Come, come, laddy, keep yer lid on and let me finish will ye? Noo, sit doon and let's see if we can find a way to keep you alive long enough to walk out the can when yer bird is done, in, whit's it? 48 hoors' time?" concluded Jamieson.

As Fear reluctantly sat back down, Jamieson, with his face bathed in a grotesque smile, continued: "That's better, ma brave soldier boy. Now, I likes you Ludovic Fear and I knows you were set up and maybe wan day I might be able to help you prove it; but for that day tae dawn yer gonna have to play ball with ma freend and help him oot with his little joab."

Jamieson stopped rocking and stared hard at Fear. He was obviously reaching the end of this one-sided exchange.

"Now here's how it's gonna pan out for you, if yer smart enough to keep yourself alive. In the tap tubing of yer bed frame is a piece of paper with the time and the place you'll be meeting my big mate three days from now. Make an arse o' that meetin' and you'll find he gives no wan a second chance, unlike my guid sel'." Jamieson took a final drag on his barely glowing roll-up and flicked it into a steel waste bin before turning his attention back to his guest.

"Now, aw I need from yous is the shake o' yer hand, soldier boy, that you'll make that meeting. Gie it tae me and I guarantees you'll walk oot the big hoose in wan piece." Again the vicious smile washed across his ruined face. With his cards now on the table, he waited to see how Fear would respond, knowing he couldn't match them.

Fear knew that his life had reached another crossroads, but what options did he have? Almost of its own volition his hand reached out to grasp Jamieson's to clinch the deal. But he couldn't help giving the handshake more power than was absolutely necessary and smiled at Jamieson's wince of pain.

"Iya," Jamieson muttered, shaking the pain out of his fingers. But he still mustered a grin of triumph. Fear might have the strength, but he had the power, as his beaten opponent knew well enough.

Putting a brave face on it, Fear snapped: "So how will I know who your mate is and what he's called?"

Jamieson laughed harshly: "Och that'll be a piece o' toffee, ma brave boy. He's got wan eye, and they calls him The Cyclops."

3

FEAR held the sand-coloured beret, gently turning it round and round in his fingers. His eyes dropped to the royal blue webbing of the stable belt that lay over his knees, its brilliant chrome buckles still shining brightly. As he stared at it he recalled his soaring pride at being badged all those years before, the faces of his former comrades fallen and still fighting flitting in and out of his mind.

His mood changed as nostalgic melancholy was replaced by the sour taste of the bitterness in which he had been immersed after his spectacular fall from grace. Jamieson had been right: what good was a Conspicuous Gallantry Cross when your reputation was in shreds?

Who had planted the Browning and the ammo in his bedside cabinet was a mystery he had turned over and over during his incarceration; yet the answer remained elusive, and he was no nearer to knowing whether it had been friend or foe.

How would he ever know when the cast of candidates for his set-up could be drawn anywhere from four continents? His triumph at being successfully promoted to Six Troop sergeant had generated animosity among some of his competitors and contemporaries who had cast doubt as to why he was selected. Since when did the Regiment give a damn about anyone's background or personal life? His illegitimacy and abandonment by his mother would surely have won him no special favours.

His left index finger traced its way around the winged dagger at the centre of the buckle and over the words: 'Who Dares Wins'.

He took a swig of the Talisker he had poured and let its intense coastal spice wash over his palate. He closed his eyes as he savoured the peatiness of the Isle of Skye's iconic malt. With Frank Sinatra's wistful "Where Are You?" in the background, it was a bittersweet moment of remembrance, regret and yearning.

Fear opened his eyes and looked around the living room of the decrepit semi-detached Victorian Villa he was now forced to call 'home'. There had once been a 'You', and as his glance fell to the pale gold pool at the bottom of his glass he felt anger and pain sear through him.

But there was still a 'You' in his life, and his eyes darted up to the wooden framed photo of his tousle-topped ten-year-old son Monty on the wall above the fireplace.

He remembered the night he had chosen that name in dedication to one of the nation's greatest ever soldiers: Field Marshal Bernard Law Montgomery, first Viscount Montgomery of Alamein. How Gina had laughed at his suggestion – until she realised he'd been totally serious.

Now Gina was about to become the former Mrs Fear, but Monty would always be his son. He winced at the shame his disgrace had caused the boy. But while the divorce papers that had been served on him in Bar-L were confirmation that there was no longer a place in Gina's heart for him, Fear realised that the offer Jamieson had made him – forced on him – might risk even the unconditional love of the son who was all he had left in his life.

He walked over to the fireplace, gently placed his glass next to the photograph and stared at his boy's impish gap-toothed grin, fighting back tears.

"Don't worry, wee man, I'll never turn my back on you, never stop lovin' you, son, never reject you like I was," vowed Ludovic Fear and raised his glass in salute towards his boy's photo.

But the thought that the matter might be taken out of his hands if Gina's drip-fed poison hit home and turned Monty against him hit him like a sledgehammer.

His eyes scanned the photo, and he saw, perhaps for the first time, the same melancholy that he stared at in the shaving mirror every morning – which left him aching with fresh guilt.

Although Monty's face was lit with a smile, that tinge of sadness was discernible, and Fear wondered if what had happened to him had indeed impacted subconsciously on his only child to the extent that his boyish features were already indelibly stained.

As his eyes took in the detail of Monty's school uniform he realised the extent his son had grown up since he had been 'away' and this Primary 6 photograph he had persuaded Gina to send him only underlined how much he had already missed.

Running a hand through his sandy mane, Fear bowed his head and faced reality. He had no option but to meet The Cyclops. No option but to listen to the offer he couldn't refuse…because it was the only one on the table.

****

The meeting had been set for 11 am the next day at The Cyclops' club, 'The Medusa', and as Fear pulled out the handwritten instructions he had found secreted in the framework of his prison bed, he smiled at the irony of his potential paymaster's choice of name for his establishment, which was located towards the west end of the city of Stirling.

Shaking his head at the gangster's choice of the snake-haired monster of Greek mythology when his own pseudonym was drawn from a similar source, Fear found it hard not to take it for granted that he would be dealing with another one-dimensional thug determined to make a fortune from a life of intimidation and mindless violence.

But then his mind raced back to his basic training at the Regimental Barracks in Hereford and heard RSM Snodgrass' terse words bark out of the flickering shadows: "Assume fuck all, boy, and you'll stay alive another day."

As the angst-ridden lyrics of Gordon Jenkins' melancholic arrangement of "The Night We called It A Day" was fading away, Fear found himself at the foot of the hall stairway, staring up at the stained glass window on the landing above. He looked closely and noticed for the first time a faint crack ran right through the ruby heart at the centre of the ornate image: a metaphor for the decline of both the house and his life? All faded hope, splendour and ambition gone to rack and ruin, he mused.

Climbing the stairs Fear heard a diesel engine outside. Taxi, he thought: some lucky bugger coming back from a night out. A car door opened, but there were no further sounds.

He reached the landing, but as he inspected the stained glass window more closely he was distracted by a nagging doubt; 'Something ain't right, mate. Taxi…where's the voices? Where's the footsteps?'

Quickly Fear made his way back down the stairs and slipped through the kitchen before unlocking his back door and letting himself out in the rear garden soundlessly. He crept along in the cover of the hedgerow angling for a view of the street in front of his house and of the powder-blue Lancia Volumex that was his pride and joy.

The street seemed quiet and, keeping to the shadows, he made his way around the side of the building and reached the front gate. Nothing but silence.

Then from the Primary School across the road came the creaking of a rusted gate, and a male, clearly the worse for wear, emerged onto the pavement, trying to do up the buttons on the front of his jeans.

Fear watched him weave unsteadily away and dismissed his suspicions. 'You're fuckin' paranoid, mate. What you expecting? The bleedin' PIRA on your tail?'

He ran his hand through his hair and gazed up at the indifferent stars in the night sky above. What, in the grand scheme of things, did he amount to? Nothing. No one was going to waste time on a disgraced soldier just released from clink.

He walked back down the side of the house and let himself back in through the back door, muttering "sufficient unto the day..." as he locked it and pushed the bolts across.

4

CLIMBING the granite steps of the four-pillared entrance to The Medusa, Fear marvelled at its ornate Victorian grandeur. Whoever The Cyclops was, his business was good. The thought also struck him that Jamieson had seriously undersold the extent of his associate's establishment.

Old habits died hard and Fear had arrived sharp for 11 am. As he stood waiting on the marble floor of the foyer, the distant sounds of a smoky female voice reached his ears.

The reception staff were clearly busy with an irate customer who was complaining in no uncertain terms about the quality of her Eggs Benedict. Fear permitted himself a slight smile at the contretemps as he scanned his chic surroundings and admired the silky sheen of a zebra-striped chaise longue.

There was still no sign of The Cyclops, nor any minions. He was sure he was at the right address. Was this some sort of set-up?

'What, in a quality gaffe like this?' snapped the voice in his head and he winced at his stupidity.

He turned his attention to the slightly husky, soulful voice coming from behind the black velvet drapes to his right.

The lyrics were unmistakeably that of Dusty Springfield's 1964 hit "I Just Don't Know What To Do With Myself", and Fear felt himself drawn to the vulnerability of the voice riding the classical piano accompaniment effortlessly to generate a heart-rending angst. The thought struck him that he was in the home of The Cyclops being drawn like a sailor to the rocks of his ruin by a Siren's song.

Fear pushed through the drapes to hear the song better. He saw that tables were being prepared for lunch, but his gaze passed over the heads of the staff to the figure at the microphone on the stage beyond them. He looked in amazement at a French-combed blonde, magnificent in white patent leather boots, a matching miniskirt and high-buttoned blouse that made Fear feel he had indeed just walked back into the 1960s.

He sat down at the nearest table, leaned back in the chair and let her voice wash over him like cool night air. Looking around him, he took in the office window that curved out high above the tables to his left and noticed the slight twitch of the black blinds that screened most of it. Presumably it was the lair of The Cyclops, but for the moment Fear was in no hurry to meet him. He was more than happy to listen to this Siren.

As she finished "Son Of A Preacher Man" Fear marked his appreciation with a spontaneous round of applause. A discreet cough heralded a voice in his ear: "Mr MacPherson sends his apologies, sir. He's just finishing some business and will be right down with you presently. In the meantime, would you like a coffee?"

Fear turned and eyed the pasty-faced young waiter trying so hard to produce a polished performance and smiled: "Skinny Mocha, single shot, no cream."

"My pleasure, sir," but his deferential nod was wasted. Fear's gaze was already wandering, for the Siren was approaching his table.

Before she reached him, she veered off and took a seat at the table opposite. She settled languorously, arranging her leather-enveloped legs with precision, before giving him a sultry smile.

Then she spoke: "So you like Dusty Springfield?"

Feeling woefully under-dressed in his suede jacket, Bengal-striped Charles Tyrwhitt shirt, Wranglers and brown brogues, Fear drank in her pulsing beauty, the immaculate make-up and the sheen of her glossy pink lips.

"To be honest I'm more of a Sinatra man, but I'd have to be a fool not to appreciate a performance like that. Your voice has a quality, I dunno it's like, aaah, honey and bourbon all in a oner, which is very impressive for 11 am in the morning! I take it you're up there again tonight?" asked Fear.

"Yeah, I do a Friday night set most weekends. I tend to go for the 60s, mix up a bit of Cilla, some Shirley Bassey, Petula Clark, but as you can probably tell by the way I dress, Dusty is my favourite!" she smiled, somehow putting the ball back in his court.

"Yeah, it works!" he replied and immediately regretted the spontaneity of his candour. Clearing his throat, he tried to recover himself: "I'm sorry, my manners are lacking. Ludovic Fear. Pleased to meet you," and he half rose to offer her his hand.

'Don't get up,' she smiled, holding up her own petite hand: "Charlie MacPherson, it's nice to meet you, Mr Fear. What a name!"

He smiled wanly back: "Yeah, it always seems to make an impact."

Charlie could see she had hit a nerve and quickly moved on: "So do you have a favourite Dusty number?"

Fear couldn't help himself and, the mischief twinkling in his eyes, he replied: "It's gotta be 'I Only Want To Be With You!'"

Her hazel gaze met his and for a few seconds their eyes remained locked, then she smiled, stood up and curtsied in mock salute: "It'll be my pleasure, Mr Fear."

Charlie turned and walked back towards the Baby Grand Piano, had a quick word with the pianist, before fixing Fear with a lingering look. He sat back in anticipation, never taking his eyes off her.

The hand that suddenly clamped onto his right shoulder almost made him jump, and when its owner walked around the table and sat down opposite him the black leather patch that sheathed his right eye made introductions unnecessary. The Cyclops had finally arrived.

5

SLOWLY MacPherson eased back, all the time assessing Fear with the piercing orb of his one eye. It was an unnerving and intimidating inspection, and Fear did not doubt that it had gained The Cyclops the upper hand in any number of encounters down the years. He returned the probing gaze with an unblinking stare. The single green orb held Fear's stony features, assessing, analysing and, it was clear, trying to unnerve him by exerting a silent stranglehold on their meeting.

Fear smiled: "Quite an establishment you have here, Mr MacPherson…" He let the sentence hang in the air, inviting a response.

MacPherson smiled, amused by Fear's conversational gambit. But before he could decide how to answer, the waiter arrived and set down Fear's Mocha, and the taut silence was broken: "The usual Americano for you, Mr MacPherson?"

The Cyclops nodded curtly and returned to the intimidating scrutiny back of his guest.

As Charlie finished her vocal, Fear once again burst into applause, aware that MacPherson's stare seemed to be intensifying. "Your daughter is a very talented young lady, Mr MacPherson," Fear observed.

After another short pause, The Cyclops spoke: "She may well be, but Charlie is not why you are here, is she, Mr Fear? Though talking of children, I hear your boy is also talented. Tennis and piano, isn't it? Very impressive."

It was a cute riposte and one that immediately warned Fear that this was a man who was not to be messed with and clearly left no stone unturned. Fear took a sip from his elegant Mocha glass, replaced it on the black tablecloth and leaned forward: "Okay, MacPherson, what do you want from me?"

The latter lifted his small espresso cup in salute: "Jamieson has made you aware, not in any great detail admittedly, that I, shall we say, require your expertise for a project I have in mind. But before we get around to that I need to know if I can trust you. I also don't appreciate people meddling when I am having summary justice meted out to individuals who must pay the price for their treachery. So, in part you will also be atoning for your folly in HMP Barlinnie. But you already know that...Mr Fear," said The Cyclops before he tugged at the black leather patch covering his right eye, which was clearly irritating him.

"So what's the nature of the business you have in mind?" asked Fear, wondering why a man with so much going for him needed a 'project'.

The Cyclops observed the sweep of Fear's admiring gaze and seemed to intuit his thought. Shifting easily in his black Armani suit, he said quietly: "One thing you must learn, Mr Fear, is that I ask the questions. What do you give the man who has everything? The answer is 'more'. But this meeting is not about me – however flattering your curiosity may be – but about you, the former SAS sergeant, Ludovic Fear.'"

The Cyclops took another sip of coffee. He was a man who liked to conduct business at his own pace.

"Tell me why haven't you gone on – what is it you ex-soldiers call it? – aah yes, 'The Circuit'? Lucrative work with former comrades and plenty of need for it with the rise of Isil?" enquired MacPherson, almost sociably but with the slight bite that Fear had noticed from the start.

Fear's jaw tightened before he answered: "I've got a feeling you're going to tell me..."

MacPherson smiled thinly: "Because you have brought shame on your regiment and none of your band of brothers wants to know you. Would that be the...gist of it?"

Fear took a deep breath then confronted the truth: "Aye, that's about the bottom line. I was set up, the ammo and the handgun were planted on me, and it's possible it may have been done by a former comrade who valued a set of stripes higher than I did. But with no proof my allegations only made things worse. I was fucked good and proper, cashiered out and then dragged through the Criminal Justice system – a disgrace to The Regiment and to my family, just like you said." Even Fear was shocked at his own frankness. Put so bluntly, it really did seem his situation was bleak beyond redemption.

The Cyclops nodded approvingly.

"Your candour does you proud. You're an outcast – beyond the pale. But I have many uses for a man of your talents, Fear, and you will be well rewarded. Should you choose not to accept my offer then you will find some very compelling reasons that will make you reconsider," concluded MacPherson and he slowly raised his right hand above his shoulders and clicked his fingers.

Within seconds a dark-suited heavy materialised and set down what looked like a silver cufflink box in front of Fear.

"Open it," suggested MacPherson amiably.

Fear decided to play the game. He slipped the lid off the box and, to his amazement and disgust, staring up at him was an eyeball, gore-smeared and attached to bloodied tendrils that trailed off over the velvet wrapping inside the container.

"Whose is it?" he demanded.

"Don't worry – it's not mine. That left the building years ago." The Cyclops grinned. He was enjoying Fear's look of shock and revulsion. He leaned across to grasp the box and, tilting it so the eyeball seemed to seek out Fear's own eyes, he went on: "I'm surprised you don't recognise it – from C Hall?"

Fear felt his fist clenching. So that's what they'd done to McCallum.

MacPherson again seemed to read his thought: "In my line of business I can't afford to let treachery go unpunished. You will be aware, Mr Fear, of the origin of my – how shall I say – *nom de guerre*: 'The Cyclops'...coming from the one-eyed monster of Greek mythology? As you can see, I make a virtue of using my own unfortunate predicament as a punishment to those who transgress against me."

Almost with tenderness MacPherson replaced the lid on the box and patted it solicitously.

He leaned forward onto the table: "I am not blessed with, nor handicapped by, a forgiving nature. But show me you are an individual I can trust and, as I said, I will reward you generously and give you the opportunity to rebuild your life, reclaim your self-respect and be the man you were... once again. I've had your record scrutinised, you see, Mr Fear. You're a killer, and whatever happened to you after you finished with The Regiment, your adjustment to Civvy Street was always going to be a problem. But I have the type of work that you were designed for, Mr Fear, and you, my friend, have no option but to take it."

This time it was Fear who leaned forward: "So you've been waiting for me as I progressed through the Criminal Justice System to the Can, waiting to set me up and then ensnare me?"

The Cyclops smiled and nodded in confirmation.

"I have followed your progress with great interest and read about your trial through the pages of the *Daily Telegraph*. When it became clear you were heading for Barlinnie I knew we would get to know each other, one way or another," and The Cyclops chuckled in amusement at his own remark.

Fear remained poker-faced.

As MacPherson's laughter subsided he quickly returned to business: "It's unfortunate that your marriage to the lovely Gina has disintegrated on the back of your personal misfortune, but now you need some gainful employment to help you pay your way and help little Monty have the life he deserves. As a father, Mr Fear, I am acutely aware of how expensive being a parent can be," finished MacPherson, his words almost kindly.

But Fear knew exactly what was being implied: "So I accept your 'work', as you call it, or my family come under threat?"

MacPherson smile was nearly amiable: "I am sure it will never come to that, Mr Fear."

He put the box into his pocket and replaced it with a plain white envelope.

"Take it. It contains the details of your first job and a generous payment in advance of services to be rendered and, of course, in expectation of a satisfactory outcome. You have a trip to Aberdeen ahead of you, where you will help take care of a rather annoying individual who has–"

Fear couldn't help himself interrupting: "Transgressed against you?"

"Indeed! Take care of this issue and report back to me here three days from now. If this itch is not scratched within that period then…" MacPherson let his veiled threat slip off into silence.

He abruptly pushed his chair back and got to his feet: "Now, if you'll excuse me, I must talk to my daughter about tonight's set." He reached out his hand. "Do we have an understanding, Mr Fear?"

"What choice do I have?" responded Ludovic Fear, reaching for the envelope but leaving MacPherson's outstretched hand hanging in the air.

As he was turning away from the table, he stole a last look at MacPherson's daughter, chatting with the pianist on the stage.

But before Fear had moved MacPherson's taunting voice assailed his ears once again: "Oh…and Mr Fear…"

Slowly he turned back to face The Cyclops once more.

"I will need proof of your mission's success…" and as that menacing smile crept over his face again, MacPherson stroked the silver box with unrestrained relish.

From her raised vantage point on the stage Charlie's gaze sought Fear's as he again turned her way…this time a smile was beyond him.

6

THE wind blowing in off the foam-flecked North Sea was cold enough to cut them in two, but the reward for their patience was now coming into sight.

Over 50 yards above them on top of the cliffs a light flashed from the ruined stone castle sentry box, confirming to the arriving fishing boat that the welcoming committee was at hand. Menzies clapped a thermal woollen beany to his bald dome and flashed a smile at the thought of the business that was about to be conducted and the lucrative gains it would bring him and his men.

Up here on the rugged North East Coastline the opportunities to land illicit cargoes away from the prying eyes of Police Scotland were becoming ever more plentiful, given the swingeing cuts made to the nation's new national force by the despised English chief constable, Sir Simon Towers.

The cuts had diluted the local knowledge and geographical awareness, which had previously been an integral part of the region's Grampian Police, while the trust of the local communities such as that of nearby Stonehaven had also been weakened by the use of 'Weegie' officers drafted up from Glasgow and other parts of the country. Their startling ignorance of local customs and arrogance towards the natives, whom they viewed almost as country bumpkins, further impacted their effectiveness.

All of which had allowed Gordy Menzies to prosper and build his illicit trade. He had been amazed by the speed at which his operation had grown as his 'business' links with his new Russian friends had developed. The quality and quantity of the coke and heroin they supplied dramatically increased his share in the lucrative lowland market, especially as he cut them ruthlessly.

But he was now in need of a new homegrown partner after his recent falling out with that treacherous one-eyed bastard MacPherson. The trouble that had brewed between them after a dispute over percentages still rankled. His florid features stinging from the assault salty wind's lash, Menzies cursed out loud in his broad North Eastern accent: "Fuckin' Cyclops, I'll have yer other eye oot if you ever traipse up Stoney way," and he spat onto the glinting silvery shingle of the beach.

Menzies was looking forward with special relish to the arrival of tonight's cargo, for in it, thanks to his newfound Russian friends, would be an arms cache that would both make him and his lads secure as rulers of the burgeoning north eastern drugs trade, and allow him to send The Cyclops a message he wouldn't forget.

With a glance at his surroundings, Menzies allowed himself a glow of satisfaction at his situation. Above him loomed Dunottar Castle, known as Dun Fhoithear in the Gaelic – fort on the shelving slope. Its position on a rocky headland just two miles away from the former fishing port of Stonehaven had proved the perfect landing point for his cargo.

It could only be accessed from the mainland by a jaw-dropping half-mile high footpath over the 'Fiddle-Head' on the promontory from the car park along the coastal road, so any unwanted arrivals from the mainland could be spotted well in advance. The two-mile cliff-top pathway from the castle to Stonehaven offered a long-forgotten escape route that the 'eediots' in Police Scotland, as Menzies liked to call them, had apparently no knowledge of, while the secluded cove he stood in provided the perfect landing point for his highly valuable contraband.

Glancing up at the Sentry Box perched on the castle's towering walls, Menzies checked that the flashlight was continuing to pulse its reassuring guidance to their visitors. He found himself marvelling that almost 300 years after the first Jacobites had used Dunottar's sheltered bay to land arms to help fuel their uprising, here he was similarly engaged in an illicit activity.

His musings were interrupted by a yell: "'S black as the earl o' hell's weskit," Hughie Paton shouted into Menzies' ear in the Doric vernacular that almost provided the North East with a language of its own, his hulking presence temporarily shielding the boss from the wind's sawing teeth.

Menzies nodded and pulled his beanie down tight for the umpteenth time: "Just get aabody ready. It's naw just the shit we're landin' the nicht Hughie. There's enough ArmaLites tae start and finish a war we' that bawbag MacPherson, if needs be, but certainly tae send him a message. So get o'er there and bring in the goods and let's get back tae Stoney and I'll be fine pleast at a guid nicht's work."

Paton tipped his head in exaggerated obeisance and crunched across the shingle to the three other members of the midnight reception party.

300 feet out in the bay the fishing boat had dropped anchor, and a small outboard motorboat was quickly filled with the cargo, covered in a waterproofed waxen sheet.

High above the bay the light from the sentry box went out, but Menzies and his cohorts were too busy anticipating landing their catch to notice.

As the motorboat spluttered to a halt and coasted the last few yards, Menzies strode across the beach and waved to the two-man crew.

"Pree-vyet!" shouted Menzies, trying out his newfound Russian for 'hello' and pleased at the sound of his efforts he waved his right hand and grinned into the near gale.

Across the foam Menzies heard the response: "Dobri vyechyer [good evening]!"

Hughie Paton's broad smile flashed Menzies' way and the big man shouted: "C'mon, boys, am wanting hame for ma braakfist. Let's get this done and we can aw get blootered o'er oor kippers!"

His two comrades roared their approval and waded out through the foam to start unloading while Menzies hollered out instructions over the wind.

The first of the Russians made his way unsteadily through the lapping water and onto the shingle and clasped Menzies' hand in a gesture of friendship. With a heavy accent he said: "All is good, my friend?"

Menzies smiled back triumphantly: "It's bloody blestyashchiy, moy drug [brilliant, my friend]!"

7

FEAR wiped the bloodied seven-inch stainless steel blade on the long grass and sheathed it. His face was set grimly as he scanned the night sky.

The sentry had been neutralised, and with the adrenalin still pumping around his body he forced himself to remain focused, as he set up his hide in the long grass 100 yards above the bay.

As he unfolded the stand below the L115A AWM (Artic Warfare Magnum) bolt-action sniper rifle his mind raced back to Baghdad 2005 and the action that had made his name in the SAS: Operation Marlborough.

While he went through the drill, his mind's eye stayed with that early morning in a baking-hot suburb of the Iraqi capital where he had been part of a four-man sniper team detailed to take out suicide bombers based in a civilian building teaming with non-combatants.

With the fourth SAS sniper held in reserve, the success of the operation had depended on the three marksmen taking out each of the suicide bombers simultaneously as the only way to stop them detonating their lethal suicide vests and wreaking carnage on the innocent civilians who surrounded them.

Firing 338 Lapua rounds that could crack an engine block from hundreds of yards away, the impact on the three insurgents from 100 yards had been devastating, and the images of their craniums turning into a pumpkin mash on impact replayed in Fear's head. But he had no regrets. He had easily squared the horrific results of his accuracy with the need to stop the fanatics from causing mass death in one of the Iraqi capital's biggest markets.

Now, he was about to unleash similar destruction, but where he could compartmentalise his actions on active service for The Regiment as legitimate in a just cause, this was far, far different.

Peering through the Schmidt & Bender sights he took in the targets: four in total, disregarding the two players in the boat, whom Fear guessed were either Russian Mafia or the remnants of a rogue PIRA unit, delivering an illicit cargo.

Unfortunately, the time it had taken Fear to remove the spotter up in his eyrie and scale the side of the castle cliff before taking up his pre-recced OP point had allowed things to get messy as one of the men from the boat was now on the beach.

With five rounds in the rifle's removable box magazine, Fear had enough to take out every one of the targets on the ground and let the remaining smuggler escape with his cargo back to the fishing boat.

'This ain't right, mate,' the voice in his head cautioned, and Fear found he was speaking to himself as his finger caressed the trigger: "What the fuck else can I do? It's them or my family, now sod off. Criminals one and all without a bleedin' conscience between the lot of them," he muttered.

But the voice in his head unhelpfully resumed: 'So what does that make you? An executioner…maybe? No…a murderer, pure and simple.'

Fear wished the voice would belt up. But he knew it was the voice of his conscience and that it was right. But he also knew there was no alternative, no way back.

****

The big Russian lit up a Sobranie cigarette, took a deep drag and passed it to Menzies, who smiled at the gold foil filter and the black body emblazoned with the Russian Imperial Eagle: "Spasibo, comrade," he grinned, nodding his head in appreciation before putting the cigarette between his lips, inhaling deeply and billowing the smoke back out, watching with a sigh of satisfaction as Hughie waded out to unload the cargo.

The other Russian remained in the small boat's prow ready to unload, but as Hughie reached out his arms to take the first package a crack rang out, and the back of Hughie's head was blown off in an explosion of tissue and bone. The impact thrust the body forward into the boat like a rag doll.

"Whit the fuck?" spluttered Menzies, throwing down his Sobranie and staring around him in search of their assailant. But before he could react further, two more shots splintered the night, and the men who had been following in Hughie's wake were flung face down into the reddening foam.

Menzies' instinct was to make for the cover of the foot of the cliffs, but before he had taken three steps another shot rang out, and he turned to see the Russian who had just shared the smoke with him sprawled on the shingle, blood pouring from an exit wound in what was left of his skull. His fellow Russian fired up the outboard motor in panic and turned the vessel back to the trawler as fast as it would go.

For a moment Menzies ignored the carnage and the danger. He was shaking, but it wasn't fear; it was rage – rage at this savage ambush that had destroyed, in one spectacular blow, all his plans and the means to carry them out. His men were gone; his cargo was now being hastily loaded back onto the trawler. And what was worse, the arms with which he might have sought a bloody revenge were gone too. The thought that The Cyclops – he had to be the one responsible – was getting away with this ruthless carnage was too painful to bear.

Until he was reminded what real pain was. A bullet ripped through his leg, flinging him in agony onto the beach. Urgent strides crashed over the shingle towards him, and as Menzies struggled to get up a fist smashed into his jaw and sent him spinning onto his back.

Standing above him was a figure clad all in black with ice-blue eyes as cold and bleak as the night shining out through the slit in a Gore-Tex balaclava.

As he looked up into the barrel of the pistol, Menzies knew there would be no mercy for him.

Almost rigid with the fear of his impending demise washing over him like the North Sea's sub-zero thrashing waters just a few feet away, Menzies found himself mouthing words that made no sound.

At last a word formed and escaped from his constricted throat: "Why?"

"Because The Cyclops says so," came the reply with all the emotionless certainty of a death sentence. The black-clad figure raised his weapon and fired twice, sending Menzies' body into a macabre dance of death on the shingle.

8

FEAR remained in the shadows at the foot of the cliffs for just long enough to make sure that the crew of the 'trawler' were not interested in sending any landing party to avenge their fellow smugglers.

An unlikely scenario, since the cargo had returned to its mother ship in full, and before long the trawler was heading back out to sea, the noise of its engine drowned out by the increasingly rough seas.

Bending over the corpse, Fear pulled the gleaming blade from its sheath and held it above Menzies' lifeless eyes. Gritting his teeth in revulsion, he knew that he had no option but to scoop out one of the dead man's eyes so that The Cyclops could have his trophy and the proof that Fear had carried out his instructions...to the letter. He knew that he had no time to debate the rights and wrongs of such a brutal course of action, and quickly he set to work with the blade before enveloping Menzies' right eye in a small plastic bag.

His own overalls and gloves ensured that there would be no cross-contamination that would provide a clue to the identity of the corpse's butcher.

Surveying the bloody mess at the edge of the beach where Menzies' minions now lay, Fear knew that he needed to make sure that these dramatic events could be attributed to a variety of possible scenarios.

Dragging Menzies' corpse down to the edge of the beach, he set about retrieving the other corpses from the lapping waves and laying them out next to their leader's body.

When it came to the fourth body, Fear rifled the dark anorak of the man he'd watched supply Menzies with the cigarette and pulled the packet from the inside pocket. The Sobranie brand confirmed his suspicions of a Russian connection. After a further search he discovered some papers purportedly belonging to a St Petersburg fisherman called Yuri Borsov.

Methodically Fear ripped open the anorak and pulled the sweat top underneath up above the dead man's chest to reveal an artistically inked rose on the Russian's chest – the classic initiation tattoo of the Russian Mafia.

"I thought so," Fear muttered, relieved that he'd killed a gangster rather than a fisherman.

He knew the inevitable in-depth criminal investigation would follow the minute the bloodied remains of Menzies and his men were discovered, spread out on the shingle of Dunottar Castle's beach. He needed to do enough to blur the lines of inquiry and to stop fingers being pointed closer to home.

His main problem revolved around the type of weapon and calibre of ammunition by which the deceased had met their grizzly fate. The AWM and its deadly payload would have the authorities asking themselves some interesting questions.

Fear hoped that by choosing the Russian manufactured GSh-18 for Menzies' execution he would nudge the investigating team in the direction of a falling out among thieves as a deal gone badly wrong. Leaving Yuri Borsov's ID documents on the corpse would also help deflect attention in an international direction.

Unfortunately, the removal of Menzies' eye would probably undo that. He would just have to hope that no one in the investigation knew of The Cyclops' unique calling card.

As he used some broken foliage to scuff over the marks caused by dragging the gang leader's body, Fear shook his head in resignation that he had now been well and truly sucked into MacPherson's cruel game.

Whatever the true nature of their business and their identities, Fear had to accept that he had become no more than a gun for hire, a trained assassin whose lethal expertise could be bought with no questions asked. There was no way he could airbrush over what he had just done in this deserted cove.

He may have proved his effectiveness and his loyalty to MacPherson, but that wouldn't be the end of it. He had no doubt that the expertise he had been so handsomely remunerated for would be soon put to the test again – and with this night's work done and his family still under threat, he was even more entangled.

9

ROUND the block the bicycles glided, the two boys riding them filling the air with their laughter.

This was suburbia, the perfect place to raise a family in a safe environment where kids could play on the streets outside their homes or round the corner at the estate's custom-made playground.

Looking out of the lounge's impressive bay window, Gina checked her watch: "8.15 pm, Monty. You're late again and on a school night too. Where are you, boy?"

But Gina's fears were soon allayed when her son and his friend cycled back into view. The boys waved to each other as their paths diverged, and they headed for their respective homes.

It was then that Gina noticed the sleek, classic lines of the British Racing Green Jaguar parked in the bay just 50 yards to the right of her house. A man got out and started walking towards Monty, who had just dismounted his cycle at the front path outside number 33 Wallace Park.

He was a striking individual, immaculately dressed in a black designer suit and shirt, with jet-black, slicked-back hair and dark stubble; but it was the black leather patch over his right eye that really grabbed Gina's attention.

Hunkering down, The Cyclops smiled kindly at the little boy and patted him on the shoulder: "Hello there, you must be Monty. Your daddy has told me all about you."

Monty was intimidated by the man's unnerving appearance and quickly glanced towards the window of number 33, knowing instinctively that his mother would be looking out for him.

MacPherson followed Monty's worried gaze and connected his single piercing eye with Gina's concerned stare.

Then MacPherson turned back to the slight but wiry lad, smiled once again and said: "I think you better put your bike away and I better go and speak to your mummy, but I have a little present for you. So if you're quick and your mummy invites me in for a cup of tea maybe we can see what it is? How would that be, Monty?"

Again the boy hesitated, wary of the stranger with the pirate's eye-patch. Seeing the look of fascinated horror, MacPherson smiled reassuringly: "Don't worry about my eye. Once upon a time I had a little accident but..." He paused for effect before continuing: "I'll let you into a little secret, young man; because I eat loads of carrots I think I can see better with one eye than most people can with two!" and then he laughed light-heartedly in a way that put Monty at ease and also drew a warm smile.

MacPherson ruffled his chestnut brown mop and walked with him towards the front door. It was already open and Gina stood there with her arms folded. MacPherson, attempting to put her at ease, inclined his head respectfully. "It's Gina, isn't it?"

"And who's asking?" Gina's second-generation Italian blood was pulsing and her dark eyes flashed with maternal fire at the stranger's over familiarisation with her son.

As the words left her mouth, Monty darted in the front door and flitted round behind his mother.

MacPherson seemed unabashed by his reception.

"Obadiah is my name and I work with your husband; but please, just call me MacPherson," he said, smiling disarmingly at Monty peering out from behind his mother. "The fact is," he confided, "I hate my first name and prefer it not to be used."

He pulled a comic face that made Monty laugh and went a long way to breaking the ice.

His opening gambit was working, and this time, trying desperately not to fixate on his eye-patch but clearly intrigued, Gina almost allowed herself a genuine smile: "You'd better come in then, Mr MacPherson."

MacPherson soon made himself comfortable in one of the large white leather settees that faced each other either side of an impressive mahogany coffee table and accepted the offer of tea.

After sipping from his cup, MacPherson gently put the red and white flowered mug back down on the tray and, seeking out Gina's scrutinising stare, said "Nice cuppa. Thanks. Now, why am I here? Given that Ludovic and I are going to be working quite closely together and I was in the neighbourhood, I thought it would be an opportunity to drop in and introduce myself. I hope you don't mind me taking the liberty, but I like to think it's just courtesy to introduce yourself to the family of a..." Then MacPherson paused adroitly for effect, before adding: "colleague."

There was something disconcerting about the way he had emphasised the word and Gina decided it was time she pressed this unnerving man: "And what exactly is the nature of your business, Mr MacPherson?"

He was ready for her and, plucking a bit of oose off his immaculately-pressed suit trousers, MacPherson replied: "I own The Medusa hotel, restaurant and club at the top of the town, and I have taken your husband on as our new Security

Consultant. I followed Ludovic's case through the legal system and I felt he was very harshly treated. A hero, chewed up and spat out but by the very people and establishment who had lauded him. For me, Gina – if I may?" MacPherson enquired respectfully before taking her slightly coquettish smile as a signal he could and continued: "For me, everyone deserves a second chance, especially a family man, who has risked his life for his country all over the globe."

MacPherson had chosen his words carefully, and now he studied Gina's reaction, her hands intertwined in her lap, her fingers twitching slightly.

"I appreciate your courtesy, Mr MacPherson, but really there was no need. Ludovic and I are separated and have been since…" Gina let the sentence die as she realised Monty was listening intently.

MacPherson nodded sympathetically. "Don't worry, I know. No need to spell it out. I just wanted to reassure you that there is a way for Ludovic to – how shall I say – aah yes, rebuild his life, and I am very happy to give him that opportunity."

"That's very good of you," Gina said, still eyeing up the stranger and trying to decide what she thought of him.

"It's entirely in my own interests," MacPherson said, finishing his tea and getting to his feet.

"Now, call me old-fashioned, but I believe a visitor should bring a gift with him. I have a little something in my car if you'd like to come and get it."

He looked encouragingly from mother to son.

'Can I, mum? Pleeeease?" Monty stood by his smother twisting his hands in excitement.

Seeing the doubt on Gina's face, MacPherson quickly said: "Why don't you both come?"

Not seeing a way of saying no without causing offence, Gina agreed, and the three of them walked down the street to the Jaguar. MacPherson opened the boot, pretending not to notice the impression the car was making. He reached in and picked up a long, flat package.

"That's for you, young man," he said, handing it to Monty. "And for the lady of the house…" With the air of a magician he produced an exquisite pot plant.

Gina took it with a smile of genuine pleasure. Their meagre budget didn't allow for such little luxuries and she knew at once where she would put it. Meanwhile Monty was tearing off the brown paper wrapping and exclaimed: "Look at this, mum!" It was a Roger Federer junior tennis racket.

"You shouldn't have," Gina said, but couldn't deny her pleasure at Monty's joy.

"What do you say, Monty?"

"Thank you!"

"That's all right, son. And don't worry," he added to Gina: "I have a daughter myself but a good bit older than your boy. I know how important it is to give them all the support you can when they find something they're good at. Anyway, I won't take up any more of your evening. But anyway, can I thank you for your time and the tea? I better not delay bed any longer, especially on a school night!" MacPherson said, moving to the driver's door.

Smiling her gratitude at his thoughtfulness, Gina was nonetheless aware that she was still being assessed by that single, disconcerting eye and realised that a part of her was enjoying the sensation. She took his hand when it was offered, receiving a light handshake.

"Good-bye, Gina; I hope we meet again sometime soon," said MacPherson, slipping into the driver's seat and giving a smile and a wave to Monty.

Gina watched as the green Jaguar drive off, then bent to retrieve the discarded wrapping paper and led Monty, playing imaginary cross-court back-hands, back into the house.

Although impressed at the presents, she had a nagging doubt that they were too generous.

"Now, Monty, homework while I get your supper on. And please put that racket down before you break something with it."

Still wondering, she shut the door behind them. She had to admit, despite his polite and considerate conversation, there was definitely something disconcerting about MacPherson that she couldn't quite put her finger on.

Gina reflected that perhaps that was because she had become far too used to the bluff, raucous camaraderie of The Regiment and those who had been her husband's colleagues and, up until recently, so she thought, friends.

Yet for all his refinement and his consideration, Gina couldn't help but feel that there was a sense of detached menace about MacPherson. And how on earth did the somewhat creepy man with the eye-patch know that Monty was such a tennis fanatic?

10

MacPherson lifted the glass of red to his lips, savoured the aroma of sweet berries, spices and herbs and then took a mouthful, letting the taffeta-soft tannins wash round his mouth.

For a moment he shut his eyes and enjoyed the thought that the intensity derived from some of the oldest Grenache, Syrah and Cinsault vines in France had once been a favourite of the Roman centurions, and now here he was in 2012 savouring the Cabalié in much the same way.

The harsh rap at his office door brought the moment to an abrupt end.

"Come!"

A nondescript man of medium height entered hesitantly and limped to the burgundy leather Captain's chair MacPherson's open palm indicated.

"Spill," MacPherson growled from the other side of the imposing walnut desk, as the new arrival shifted uncomfortably in his yellow and black Helly Hansen anorak that was plainly too big for him.

MacPherson lowered his slightly hooked nose to the rim of the glass to luxuriate in the Cabalié's sensuous aromas once again and waited.

After clearing his throat, the man started talking: "I followed him aw the way up tae Stonehaven and am sure he never made me, otherwise he does'ne go ahead wi' the jobe…and whit a fuckin' jobe he does!"

MacPherson brought the Dartington glass to his lips and, after he had quaffed another mouthful, placed it down sharply on a silver coaster. "Tell me the details then, Williams," he demanded.

"I got meself a brilliant wee perch that took in the whole cove and swept up tae the castle, settled in wi' the thermos o' coffee, ready to take in the show. Fuck me, it was the best night's viewin' I seen yet, boss mawn, like somethin' straight aff that Strikeback on TV," said Williams, his index finger finding its way into his mouth before his decayed teeth attempted to make a meal of it.

"Your admiration for our new friend's work is not what I'm paying you for, Williams?" said MacPherson, the drumming of his fingers on the desk's inlaid leather writing panel betraying his rising impatience.

"Of course. Sorry. Well…first he takes out their watchy, up in wan o' the castle's turrets and the next thing it's like Spiderman comin' swinging down the cliff, and then he's straight over tae the long gress and am thinkin' where the feck is he. If it was'ne for the fact I had been up there waitin' and watchin' hours before he arrived and seen wi'ma own eyes as he built himself a wee hide, I would'ne have known he wiz there at aw boss. Christ he wiz like the Wicker Man when he rose up fae it," said Williams, pausing for breath.

"So far, so good," said MacPherson, then pointed to the fridge by the door, Williams' gaze following his finger. "Get yourself a beer man; but look sharp and hopefully it will help improve your total recall," he concluded with a trace of a smile breaking at the corners of his mouth at his pop culture reference.

Williams' surprise was as obvious as his eagerness for some refreshment, and he almost tripped as he jumped up from the chair. When he opened the fridge and removed a dark bottle from it, his disappointment was clear: "Joker?" he asked of no one in particular, before almost apologetically meeting MacPherson's intimidating gaze and blurting out: "Don't suppose you've got any Tennent's, boss mawn?"

"I'd say a bottle of Joker is more appropriate for you, Williams, wouldn't you agree? You are here because we can't trust any of this information over a phone. Now take the beer, sit down, have a drink and get a fuckin' move on with your report…Charlie's set is due to start in an hour and I want some dinner before then."

Williams regained his chair, took a swig of the IPA and attempted to stifle his disgust. He then ploughed on: "Menzies and his boys were down on the beach waitin' for their cargo and then, just as they're enjoyin' a smoke wi' the Russian, he starts takin' 'em oot – wan by wan, leavin' Menzies for last, just like yous wanted boss. But that wiz worth waitin' for. Yer man scoots down through the gress and…" here Williams formed his hand into a gun, "Bang, he fires wan intae Menzies' knee, smack, he clocks him a right hawnd and wi' Menzies flat oan his back, pop, pop, he finishes him point blank to the forehead, bends doon and cuts himself a helpin o' eye! Joab done. It wiz fuckin' beautiful boss, mawn, a real pro's' joab…Skinners O'Kippen wid hae been proud o' it! If yous ask me this is a geezer who can dae anythin' you want; naebody but naebody, is safe from him, boss mawn," Williams concluded with a grin.

His reverence for Fear's work was now irritating MacPherson.

"He's meant to be the best. That's why I hired him. But what about the Russians, how did he leave things with the bodies?" snapped The Cyclops, rubbing his right index finger over his patch.

"He's popped the wan o' them who's come ashore, but the other one in the delivery boat fucked off sharpish. Then, I'm thinkin', he's laid the bodies out like there has been some kind o' firefight and the survivors have fucked off oot tae sea wi' the loot. Naw, he's covered aw the options, boss, and no way was he aware I was lying low 100 yards away watchin'."

His tale told, Williams looked up expectantly. MacPherson produced a brown envelope from a drawer and slapped it on the desk's leather inlay.

MacPherson turned the full intensity of his one-eyed stare on his minion: "You're sure about that. Williams? He never saw you?"

"100 per cent, boss mawn, 100 per cent," Williams answered, eyeing the envelope.

MacPherson pushed it towards him and watched as Williams hand shot out and grabbed it: "Finish your beer downstairs and report to Vallance on the way out. He'll give you instructions for your next job." Williams was on his feet, beer in one hand, the envelope in the other, when MacPherson spoke again.

"Oh and Williams……"

Turning, Williams cradled his beer as if it would provide him with some protection from what he was about to hear next: "Yes boss?"

"You speak of this to no one, because if you do it will be the last words you ever utter…understand?" asked The Cyclops venomously.

"Nae bother, Mr MacPherson, nae bother, Williams knows the score, boss mawn." Then he touched the bottle of beer to his forehead respectfully in an act of total supplication and limped hurriedly out of the office.

Raising the Cabalié once more to his lips, MacPherson permitted himself a wry smile. Fear had passed his first major test, and now he could proceed with the project he had been brought on board for in the first place…but not before the former soldier had passed one last test.

11

FEAR reached the black velvet curtains as the title words from "The Look of Love" floated out in that unmistakeable husky voice. He hung back, peering through the drapes at Charlie MacPherson, chanteuse, Siren and who knew what else?

She shimmered in a silver-sequined dress that was cut just above the knee and rose to her elegant, swanlike neck. As the saxophone sounded out a shudder ran down Fear's spine. He couldn't linger behind the curtains forever, so he pushed through and stood at the back of the room.

Gracefully Charlie swayed in effortless rhythm as she started on "Love Me By Name", her hair French-combed perfection, her thick black eyeliner emphasising the beauty of her hazel eyes, which now picked him out across the auditorium.

Fear realised that he was under scrutiny himself and that he was smiling involuntarily, unable to hide his appreciation for either her performance or her appearance. But the line of her sight had not gone unnoticed and The Cyclops' eye stared icily at him from his table just to the left of the stage.

Fear turned his head slightly in MacPherson's direction, locked eyes with him and gave a slight nod of recognition. Then, slipping his right hand inside the pocket of his jacket to make sure the box was still there, he skirted his way through the busy tables at which diners were clearly captivated every bit as much as he had been by Charlie's performance.

Reaching MacPherson's table, Fear pulled out the chair opposite The Cyclops, sat down and, removing the box from his jacket, pushed it across the cloth until it came to rest under the subdued glow of the small table light.

"Your proof," said Fear, not bothering to hide his disgust.

MacPherson made no response but cut another mouthful from his steak and gazed up at his daughter as he began to chew. He washed the last piece of meat down with a draft of red and carefully dabbed at his mouth to make sure he wasn't now sporting a ruby-red moustache. Then, still not bothering to look at Fear or reach for the box just a few inches from his hand, he asked: "You admire my daughter or her performance, Mr Fear?"

"She has an undeniable talent and a talent that should grace a bigger stage, surely you would agree with that?" responded Fear.

This time MacPherson did look at him and replied, betraying barely concealed anger: "Answering a question with another question is no answer at all, my friend; but then you'd know that from your training with The Regiment, wouldn't you?"

To Fear's surprise, he reached for the bottle of wine and poured a generous measure into an unused crystal glass.

"Have you sampled the delights of The Black Stump, Mr Fear?" with the veneer of his self-control once again immaculate, MacPherson pushed the glass towards him.

Fear raised it and breathed in, then grinned: "Shiraz Durif, if I'm not mistaken?"

"Correct." MacPherson raised an eyebrow in surprise.

"We enjoyed a glass or two in The Regiment after a job well done." He took an appreciative swig, then put his glass down.

"Aren't you going to open the box?" he said, raising his own eyebrows.

MacPherson shook his head.

"I need no confirmation of the excellent work you did on Menzies and his teuchters. Your professionalism has been confirmed and the credentials that made me seek your services out established, beyond question. Now I have another matter that requires your attention before we are ready to proceed to the meat of things – the job you were ultimately recruited for."

Fear's normally blank face couldn't help showing his surprise at the realisation his foray up in the North East had been monitored, but before he could speak The Cyclops raised his right index finger: "Aah, this is my favourite," he said, pushing his chair back and folding his arms across his chest as Charlie started on the melodramatic notes of "All I See Is You". They both sat transfixed in admiration at the heartrending quality of Charlie's interpretation of the Italian-style ballad Dusty Springfield made a Top Ten hit in 1966.

Resisting the strong urge to feast his eyes on the singer, Fear glanced at Charlie's father and noticed him dabbing his good eye with the corner of his napkin. What did they say about the hardest men being sentimentalists at the core? MacPherson was undoubtedly a besotted father. Perhaps that's why he kept her locked away in the gilded cage of The Medusa, instead of letting her fly free to prove her talent in the wider world.

There was no mistaking how proud MacPherson was of his daughter, and Fear found himself asking, 'Why keep her locked up?' but quickly answered his own question: 'None of your business, pal,' and took solace in the bramble aroma and silky finish of his glass of Black Stump.

As Charlie's set drew to a heartrending end with "If You Go Away", Fear found himself staring into the black tablecloth, which now seemed a vortex for his swirling emotions.

Maybe it was the haunting lyrics of the song or Charlie's aching interpretation of it that ended in the smoky, whispered, arms-open plea of 'Please don't go away' that somehow summoned up Gina's face and that of Monty as well.

But as the applause began to die down, MacPherson broke in on his thoughts to continue the earlier conversation: "I'm glad you enjoyed that, and to go back to your unasked question, yes, Mr Fear, I did have you surveilled. Even the SAS, when they are not expecting it, can be observed. But let's turn our attention to your family shall we? I took the liberty of paying Gina and young Monty a visit while you were away. Monty. I take it it's Montgomery and not Montague? Nice kid. I can see a bit of you in him – whereas his good looks obviously come from his mother. I wouldn't give up on your marriage just yet, if I were you. I think it could be salvaged."

Fear's patience broke and before he knew it he was on his feet facing The Cyclops, with his chair clattering over behind him.

"Relax, man, nothing to get upset about" MacPherson said, nodding to the overturned seat to indicate he wished his guest would sit down again. "I simply made a courtesy call, introduced myself as your new employer and did everything I could to convince Gina you now have the means to provide for her and your son. So I suggest you calm down and finish your wine. We don't want a scene, especially with Charlie about to join us," said MacPherson amiably.

"I think I've had enough of you and your games for one night, MacPherson," Fear said emphatically, but as he pushed the chair back in under the table, he felt a hand on his elbow and a velvet voice purred in his ear, "You don't fancy my company, Mr Fear?" asked Charlie mischievously.

He swung round and the proximity of her beauty made him gasp. It posed an impossible dilemma, but in the end he grimaced: "I'm sorry, Charlie, there is somewhere I need to be. If you don't mind me saying I thought you were..." and Fear found himself fumbling awkwardly for the right word. Acutely aware her father was just yards away, he stammered out: "...I thought you were fantastic. Just a shame your audience is measured in tens not thousands."

"Why...thank you, Mr Fear," she said in a husky voice, with just a hint of a belle from the American Deep South in it that sent tremors through his body.

Shrugging awkwardly, he said: "Sorry. It's my loss but needs must," and with that he stalked off.

12

FEAR took a deep breath, rang the doorbell and stepped back from the front door.

Through the frosted glass he saw Gina's silhouette approaching and felt his heart hammering.

She opened the door, clearly not surprised he had turned up.

"I wondered how long it would take you to come round, Ludovic. I guess you better come in," she said and although Gina smiled there was no warmth there.

He followed her through to the kitchen and watched as she put the kettle on, feeling uncomfortable at the thought of taking a seat in his own home – or, the place that he had once considered home.

"Take a seat," she said over her shoulder. "You know I can't stand you hovering."

Fear pulled up a stool at the breakfast bar and soon they were facing each other over mugs of coffee.

Then in a rush he couldn't help himself and burst out: "How are you, Gina? How's Monty settling into P7?"

Gina took a sip from her own mug, The Wimbledon memento he had bought her on their trip to the Championships back in 2009.

Seeing his glance, she managed a brief smile and murmured: "Good times, Ludo."

She met his gaze and for moments they said nothing, clutching at their coffee mugs awkwardly.

The voice in his head lamented: 'Christ, where do I start?' But he needn't have worried, for Gina took control of proceedings…just like she'd always done.

"We met your new boss, Mr MacPherson. Pity about the eye-patch! Monty thought he was a pirate. But still, a pirate with a job in his gift. So, you're now a Security Consultant. A grand title covering a multitude of sins I bet, Ludovic…" she left the implication hanging in the air.

Fear looked over his mug at her dark Italian beauty and realised just how much he had missed her. It hit him hard and, as it did, he pushed his hands through his hair. He did not want the conversation snagged on his new job.

Gina looked at him quizzically. "You always ruffle your hair when you're struggling for an answer, Ludo; did you know that?" she asked.

"I'm sorry, I didn't know I was so…easy to read," he replied blankly, and then his right hand seemed to reach out of its own volition for Gina's hand. He felt her flinch, but she did not draw away.

"Well, I didn't read that," she said.

Into the void he spoke: "I miss you, Gina, I miss you both – so much…so very much. What can I say? I'm sorry, love. I'm so sorry."

She turned her dark gaze on his and he saw the sadness swimming in her gaze before the anger sparked: "Sorry for what? Ruining our lives? Bringing shame on us as a family? The bullying Monty has had to endure at school? Not being there? Which particular part of the mess you've made of everything do you want to begin with, Ludovic?"

He knew how angry Gina had been from her rage-filled letters, which had kept arriving at Barlinnie after she'd stopped visiting. He'd hoped her anger had been sated by now but then who was he fooling: 'Fuck's sake, Ludovic, that's why you're staying down the Riverside in a broken-down Victorian Villa,' chimed the voice in his head with its usual immaculate timing.

"Look, I know I messed up, Gina, but..." before he could continue she interrupted, her voice quivering with emotion as she began to shout, such was the rawness of her feelings: "But now you have a new job, a new house and everything is going to be rosy? Well I've got news for you, Ludovic Fear: after two wasted years of life things have moved on for us."

The increase in decibels brought the sound of feet coming down the stairs and in ran Monty.

"Dad, Dad, you're back," he yelled, dashing over to throw himself into Fear's embrace.

Looking over Monty's dark pelt of hair, Fear could see that Gina's rage was unabated.

"Darlin', it's late on a school night, and you don't need all this excitement or you'll never get up in the morning," she said.

Monty looked up, as if to appeal against his mother's diktat. Fear smiled down at him, his love for Monty burning out through him, and a foot away the strength of his emotion brought tears spilling down Gina's face.

Surprised by the sudden change in his wife's demeanour, Fear concentrated on his son: "Look, pal, your mum's right; it's late and we'll have plenty of other times to catch up. Maybe I could come round and take you for a kickabout at the Haws Park and then an ice cream up at the Allan Water Café?"

Monty looked anxiously at his mother, who gave a watery smile of acquiescence.

Fear felt elated but told himself not to show too much. 'Ask about school,' his inner voice reminded him.

"So how's P7 going?"

Holding Monty in front of him, Fear saw how much his son had grown while he had been incarcerated and realised just how much he had missed him. Not for the first time, he cursed The Cyclops for stopping him from going to see his son as soon as he got out of Barlinnie. He could understand Gina's anger. It all must have seemed a terrible abandonment.

"P7's great, Dad. We've got a new teacher – Mr Jones. He shouts a lot and yesterday one of the boys was crying in the cloakroom after he gave him a row!"

Fear smiled and ruffled Monty's tousled mop of hair: "I feel for the poor man. You must drive him crazy. But time for bed, young fella. Give me a quick kiss good night."

A final wave from the foot of the stair after more reassurances of a return visit left him back at square one in the kitchen.

Gina, her composure regained, had busied herself making a fresh coffee and, pushing it his way, she sat down once again.

"He's grown a lot," Fear said, almost in a whisper, his words clearly admitting that he had missed so much.

Gina's gazed at him for a moment, as though trying to make up her mind about something. Eventually she spoke: "Look, Ludovic, there is something I have to tell you and… well…there's no easy way to do it."

He met her words with silence.

"I'm sorry, but I've met someone else," she said flatly.

Fear was stunned. Again his right hand involuntarily shot through his shaggy mane: "Jeez…well how did that happen?" was the best he could do.

"He's a single dad on the local PTA and I guess we have…" and this time Fear finished the sentence for her: "…a lot in common."

13

FEAR looked out across the hills and drummed his fingers on the three-spoked steering wheel of the Volumex, his impatience building as he tried to force the disastrous visit to Gina out of his mind and bring all his concentration to bear on the meeting ahead.

Finally the Black BMW 3 Series he had been waiting for turned into the car park, and he saw that The Cyclops, who was sitting in the passenger seat, had brought company. He was finally to meet MacPherson's number two, known only to him as Vallance.

Nestled on the slopes of the Ochills some miles away from the small Victorian spa town of Bridge of Allan, The Sheriffmuir Inn overlooked the site of the 1715 Battle of the same name, which had provided the pivotal moment of the first Jacobite Rising.

The premises had also been famously owned by the 1970s TV wrestler Andy Robin and his grappling bear Hercules, but now it was one of the most popular country eating venues in the area, though still sufficiently off the beaten track to provide a discreet meeting place.

Fear got out of his vehicle and eyed the new arrivals as The Cyclops and his right-hand man crunched over the car park towards him.

They headed for one of the wooden tables situated just outside the old drovers' hostelry, which provided a stunning view over a nearby lochan framed by the pastel shades of the Perthshire hillsides.

"A pleasant enough evening for a wee rendezvous. I hope you'll let my friend, Mr Vallance, treat us to a pint?" asked The Cyclops in his deceptively amiable way, which Fear instantly wondered if he'd employed on Gina when he had come calling a few nights earlier.

Fear looked MacPherson's sidekick up and down: shaved head, scarred face, huge shoulders, muscle-bound arms covered with Celtic tattoos and a Mexican moustache – the henchman from Central Casting. Clearly Vallance was a man not to be messed with. He nodded his acceptance: "A Caesar Augustus, if they've got any on draught, would go down well."

MacPherson indicated a bench nicely positioned to catch the evening sun.

"How appropriate, Mr Fear. Did you know that we are surrounded by evidence of the Roman invasion of Scotland? Back in 80 AD the first wave of legions marched north through the 'Stirling Gap' from Camelon and built their marching camps in Dunblane, Doune and the huge fort at Ardoch near Braco, while also erecting a line of watchtowers along the Gask Ridge towards Perth." MacPherson made a panoramic sweep with his right hand: "So, although people may think of Sheriffmuir only in Jacobite terms, when it comes to history it is the Romans who left a greater mark on the landscape."

After a short pause, which Vallance used to assess Fear, MacPherson's eye rested on his right-hand man, waiting patiently for the rest of the drinks order. "Why don't we join Mr Fear in his historical appreciation. Three pints of Caesar, if you don't mind, Marty, and that will allow me to start filling our friend in on our plans."

"Nae bother, boss," replied Vallance curtly and headed inside to get the round. Fear felt MacPherson's one-eyed gaze upon him.

Steepling his hands on top of the wooden table, MacPherson cut to the chase: "I have another itch that needs scratching. It is a matter of control and a good bit closer to home than Dunottar Castle!"

Fear cocked his head to show he was listening but remained silent.

MacPherson continued: "I enjoy protection rights over the local Post Offices in the outlying areas around Stirling, but I'm afraid that a troublesome individual by the name of Jimmy Bancroft has decided to try and disrupt my little enterprise. He is also supplying drugs to local school kids and I want something done about it. I would like a little imagination employed in the process of picking him up, but Bancroft must be alive and kicking when you bring him to me. You see I don't only want him destroyed: I want Bancroft humiliated. Any suggestions?"

"If you tell me where this Bancroft lives I can easily set him up with something that will make life very difficult for him." He paused. "Am I correct in thinking that you do have a conscience?" asked Fear, still slightly surprised at his previous remark about the schoolkids.

MacPherson smiled: "Look, I have no problem making money from the drugs trade, but I do have a problem when some idiot starts dealing to schoolkids. There'll be some younger than your lad, Monty. But it's not just to protect the kids. Selling at the school gates is bad for business, and it brings unwanted attention from the powers that be. When it is combined with some local thug getting above his station and ripping off my loyal customers, enough, Mr Fear, is a fucking enough," summed up The Cyclops, his anger at the situation starting to show.

But before he could elaborate, Vallance arrived and laid the beers and, after MacPherson had taken a draft from his glass, he turned to his subordinate: "Marty, why don't you give our new Security Consultant the details of his next…client?"

"Decent pint, that," muttered Vallance, setting his pot down and wiping his mouth with the back of his hand: "Bancroft is strictly low grade muscle wi' fuck all brains… otherwise he would'ne be making the mistakes he's just made. But he's starting to get a wee following with the next generation of scum from around the old mining villages and we need that sorted. You understand that, Mr Fear?" he said, placing sarcastic emphasis on the 'Mr'.

As a small but stinging breeze blew up, Fear pulled the zipper of his Barbour up and tugged down his baseball cap until it shaded his eyes slightly, took a mouthful of his pint and let his eyes survey the two men sat opposite him: 'Take your time, mate, and let them wonder what is going on inside yer head,' suggested the voice there.

"So do you have his home address, the name of the boozer he drinks in, family details and when he's out and about?" asked Fear flatly.

MacPherson nodded his head towards Vallance: "Give him the dossier, Marty. As you know, Mr Fear, we always do our homework…thoroughly." Then he winked at his number two.

Vallance's right hand was already halfway inside his jacket before MacPherson had completed his prompt: "You'll find the whole shootin' match inside there," he said, smiling knowingly as he slapped a manila envelope on the table.

Fear let it lie where it was and looking across the table said: "You say you want him brought to you alive. That's not a problem. But there will be the next time you want someone taken out. This business of taking an eye from your victims can't go on. Surely it can't have escaped you; all you're doing is leaving a calling card for the cops. It won't take long before some smartarse CID is going to put two-and-two together and get The Cyclops – and possibly me. Which isn't going to happen."

MacPherson continued to examine his immaculately manicured fingernails as he replied: "Do you think that my – how shall I call them – ah yes..." and The Cyclops paused to supply a quotations gesture with the two central fingers of each hand: "...my victims are about to complain? Correct me if I'm wrong, Mr Fear, but without a complainer the police are going to struggle to make anything stick. Sweet Christ, the mess Police Scotland are in, with that English idiot Towers in charge, I could be made of Teflon. Besides, it appears they're too busy stop searchin' every teenager in sight to bother with us. I would also like to – pardon the pun – caution you, with this: do you think I don't have a little insurance policy tucked away up at Randolphfield? The resentment that the local coppers feel at the way they are being treated post-amalgamation has made them vulnerable to a little persuasion...if you catch my drift."

Fear's lips moved to part with an answer, but before he could manage one, Vallance slammed down his pint pot, sending some Caesar Augustus over the rim of the glass and onto the wooden table, unhelpfully running over the edge of the envelope: "Will I tell him or you, boss?" he asked almost gleefully.

MacPherson wiped a fleck of beer from the back of his hand: "Among the criminal fraternity, Fear, it's important to send a message. We are building something here in Stirling, and it's based on fear – again, no pun intended – and efficiency. Someone fucks with us and we take an eye for an eye and whether they live to see the next day is another matter!" and with that master and sidekick both exploded into laughter.

Despite himself, Fear found a smile cross his face and nodding his head in acceptance he reached for the envelope and, removing it from the sleeve, began to study the contents of a typed sheet of A4.

As he did so MacPherson spoke quietly into the growing breeze: "So how did your homecoming go, Ludovic? I hope my pastoral visit hasn't caused you any problems with the lovely Gina?"

Fear kept his eyes on the sheet of paper but couldn't stop a slight tremor in his hands betray the anger that MacPherson's jibe had sparked inside him. So, MacPherson had him under surveillance, even when he wasn't on active service. His mind turned back to the drunk outside the school gates opposite his house the other night.

Fear looked up: "I would prefer my private life to remain just that, MacPherson. Stand your spies down. We wouldn't want anyone to get needlessly hurt, would we?"

MacPherson finished his pint and stood up. He placed his hands on the edge of the table and leaned forward.

"Of course," he said, "and likewise, I would advise you to keep your admiration for Charlie within appropriate bounds. It's seldom good policy to go after the boss's daughter – is it, Vallance?"

"No, Boss; it ain't," growled the hulk, looking down at Fear with a sadistic leer on his face. "Her last admirer came to a right fishy end."

The two men shared a brief laugh.

"All right, Fear. Point made, I trust. Now make sure you take care of the business in hand...ASAP."

Then with a curt nod to Vallance, he led the way across the car park back to the car.

14

FEAR watched the BMW wind its way out of the car park, but as the sleek black machine drew level with him he was treated to a taut smile by MacPherson, who also shaped the fingers of his left hand into a circle and appeared to look through it back at him. Then the vehicle headed off down the oak-lined roadway for Bridge of Allan.

"Bastard," Fear muttered, but the thought struck him that they at least shared similar situations: both their lives were dominated and made vulnerable, in almost equal measure, by women.

He pushed these unwelcome reflections aside and started the Volumex. The two-litre supercharged engine, fired by a 1983 Bosch electronic fuel injection system, gurgled into its throaty purr. 135bhp – how he ached to give it the full Monty. The thought of his son's name brought a wistful smile to his face. Monty was still the one constant in his chaotic life.

Although there was not much chance of giving the Volumex any real wellie down the winding, almost single-track road that would take him over the muir, he decided to go for the appropriate mood music. With a loud "Fuck it"

Fear shoved Deep Purple's "Live in Japan" in the CD player, then flicked to "Highway Star", tickled the accelerator and let the Lancia roar. He pressed 'Play' and prepared for the pleasure of Jon Lord's majestic keyboard solo.

The powder-blue Italian classic shot out of the car park in a shower of gravel, turning the heads of those hardy enough to be still nursing their drinks outside. Fear felt slightly ashamed at playing the boy racer, but that passed as he drove away into the pastel beauty of Perthshire countryside.

At the speed he was going Fear recognised the need to keep his eyes peeled for potholes while he also scanned the horizon for oncoming traffic. The road was nearly single-track but had handily placed passing spots.

Enjoying the moment and feeling increasingly like a rally driver, he shot over the hump of a small hill and landed with a bump that brought a rebuke from his internal voice: 'For crying out loud, will you watch what you're doing with the old girl.'

He settled to a more sensible speed, freeing up more headspace to review his situation. MacPherson's warning to stay clear of Charlie was not just parental paranoia. With her undoubted beauty and intoxicating interpretations of the Sixties' classics he loved, there was no denying the attraction. But then there was Gina, and, of course, Monty. He replayed the scene in the kitchen and could almost feel his son's arms around his neck.

Waves of guilt immediately enveloped him. He shut his eyes momentarily and drew upon his years of training, mentally putting the issues into separate little black boxes. Gina was gone, already planning a new future with the bloke from the PTA, eaten up by the resentment she felt towards him for all he had put her and his son through.

Whatever happened between Gina and that bloke he was determined not to let anything stand between him and

Monty. For all the baggage he had accumulated, he wasn't going to jeopardise the most important relationship in his life. Silently Fear vowed to himself that nothing would ever get between him and his boy again.

Whilst all this was swirling in his mind, he logged a white Transit van coming up a side road from one of the many derelict farmhouses, and which seemed to be going faster than was sensible. As he passed the junction Fear's mind returned to Charlie and their last encounter at The Medusa and her father's subsequent warning to stay off the grass. Had The Cyclops really ordered the killing of a previous admirer? Was the remark about his fishy end simply a joke in bad taste, or a reference to the disposal of a body? Scotland certainly provided enough lonely stretches of water for any number of watery graves.

Fear was brought back to the present with a jolt by the unmistakable report of automatic gunfire crackling over Deep Purple.

Fear hurriedly checked his rear-view mirror as he turned off the stereo. The mental image of Charlie was immediately replaced by the sight of the white van now on his tail and closing fast. There was a figure wearing a balaclava leaning out of the passenger window doing his best to riddle the Lancia with bullets from what looked like an ArmaLite AR-18, the automatic rifle favoured by the Provisional Irish Republican Army and capable of discharging 750 rounds a minute.

It was not for nothing the rifle had become known as 'The Widowmaker' across the Emerald Sea and now it had come back to haunt him.

15

FEAR responded immediately and instinctively by putting his foot down and at the same time weaving from one side of the road to the other, trying to avoid the hail of lead being spat from the van; but with less than 25 feet of crumbling tarmacadam to play with there wasn't much chance of his pale blue pride and joy avoiding a shredding from the AR-18's lethal payload.

Whoever was in the van – and as far as his mirror revealed the pursuit vehicle was 'two up' – was determined to give him the 'good news' and reduce the Lancia to a colander, as well as Fear's coffin.

Lead exploded off the rear of the Volumex, and Fear heard glass smash as one of the vehicle's rear lights shattered, while the swarm of bullets sent up a shower of chipped stone from the dyke just in front of the Lancia.

Fear hunched over the steering wheel and stamped the accelerator to the floor. 135bhp kicked in, the torque sending a shiver of unlikely pleasure through his body as the Volumex left the Transit for dead, and the gunfire from the AR-18 soon faded into the wide blue yonder. But though the gap between the Lancia and the Transit soon stretched to over 100 yards, Fear had another problem: the hulking form of a tractor trundled out of a field a quarter of a mile in front of him and then stopped, blocking the road.

If there had been any doubt before – he might have got the clue provided by the Widowmaker wrong – the format of the ambush now provided him with all the confirmation he needed.

He had sprung a classic PIRA trap.

The war across the Irish Sea was not over for everyone. It looked as though his past had caught up with him, and a rogue Active Service Unit had come after him, determined on terminal payback for his 'work' on the Emerald Isle.

Fear reached under the driver's seat for the Browning 9mm. He had always kept a weapon taped there in every vehicle he'd driven, ever since his tours in Ulster. Ripping it out, he stuck it under his thigh in readiness.

There was no way around the tractor and as he slowed the Transit van began to close the gap. Hopelessly outgunned, Fear had no intention of being trapped like a wasp in a tin can.

He scanned the ramshackle drystone wall to his left and saw that it had collapsed a few yards ahead of him. In the field behind, a slight dip led to a copse of birches staggered around a small loch.

It gutted him to abandon the Lancia but what option did he have? He rammed on the anchors, grabbed the keys and the Browning and, making himself as small a target as possible, exited the car. He sprinted for the gap in the dyke, but his escape drew a hail of fire, and as he dived for cover he could hear the stone chippings exploding around his ears.

Safe for a moment, he reviewed his options. The field he was in was open pasture. The nearest trees were over 100 yards away. He hoped there would be enough dead ground in the dip to give him a fighting chance of reaching them and so set off in a crouching, zigzagging sprint.

As he ran, the voice in his head chipped in: 'Christ, it had to happen one day,' at the inevitably that someone from his past was bound to seek retribution. His mind replayed scenes from his two tours on the Island, searching for clues as to the identity of his pursuers.

Now it seemed that the finger of death was twitching on the trigger of an AR-18. If, as seemed likely, he was about to go down, he wanted to have some idea who was pulling the trigger.

He heard shouts from the road and stole a glance over his shoulder. His heart sank as he saw a four-man team fanning out from the gap in the wall – all of them armed with some serious hardware.

As he moved, Fear slotted a round into the chamber of the 9-milly, patted the poacher's pocket of his Barbour for the reassurance provided by one of the two other spare magazines – the third was strapped to the inside of his calf. He tried to keep them always about his person ready for the possible Doomsday scenario that was now unfolding, and this had been partly to blame for his spectacular fall from grace.

Helpfully his inner voice replayed a line of his from a particular operation in South Armagh: 'If I need more than 39 rounds, I'm fucked.'

So far he was still alive, still dangerous and was determined to sell his life dearly. If he could just make the trees, he might get out of this in one piece.

The ground now turned marshy as it dipped down towards the copse. Bullets were singing over his head and taking chunks out of the turf around him, but he was within 30 yards of sanctuary, however scanty.

He could hear the bullets smacking into the trees ahead of him, which, he told himself, was a good thing. It meant the distance was narrowing. And at last he got there and threw himself behind the first significant piece of wood that presented itself. He immediately turned, regained his balance and adopted a one knee firing position as he sighted his pursuers along the Browning's barrel.

The quarry was now no longer the prey and Fear allowed himself a wolfish smile. He lined up each of the ASU as they spread out across the muir, judging when they would become viable targets. With four against one he steadied himself for the impending CQB (Close Quarter Battle). Although the odds were steep, he still had hope that The Regiment's unique training would swing things his way. Fear moved sideways, adopting the 'Weaver Stance', which would allow him to shoot much faster and with greater accuracy. This meant that, as a skilled practitioner, Fear could double-tap a deadly head shot from over 15 feet.

He steadied himself as the first ASU man, in an old green army jacket, started to come down the gulley towards him.

"Fear, ye murderin' Brit scum, come an' get it," he screamed in an unmistakeably harsh Northern Irish accent and then let rip a burst of automatic gunfire from his Widowmaker through the branches above Fear's head.

Fear gritted his teeth, praying that he wouldn't be filleted before he had time to strike back. But although wood splintered and shredded foliage exploded all around him, he held his nerve.

Taking false security from the lack of a reply to his burst of fire the gunman continued careering down the gulley.

When he was 15 feet away, Fear opened fire: three short bursts, the first scything through the player's temple, the second and third thudding home into his chest as he staggered back, a look of surprise frozen over his bloodied features, as he fell lifeless to the sodden turf.

That was a warning to the remaining three members of the ASU that Fear was not the sitting duck they might have assumed but a lethal quarry, ready to fight fire with fire – to the death.

16

THEY paused and the figure in the middle of the shooting party, sporting a fully zipped-up Adidas tracksuit jacket and denims, dropped to one knee and indicated that he wanted his brothers-in-arms to fan out and start an encircling manoeuvre.

But one of the men, a shaggy-haired individual with a sparkling stone winking from his right ear in the last of the evening sunshine had other ideas and opened fire with his ArmaLite.

Fear suddenly remembered the identity of his pursuer and the reason behind his and his ASU's determination to wreak bloody revenge.

"That bastard Sean Doyle from 'The Creggan'!" he muttered. A host of images clamoured to be reviewed, but the desperation of his current situation meant all that had to be put to one side.

He had taken one man down, but the element of surprise was gone. His enemies knew he was armed, and they could deploy their remaining numerical superiority to good advantage. Fear had big problems.

There was no way he could hold his present position and made a half-turn to sweep the area behind him in search of a better defensive position.

Nothing doing. His only option was to try and stay in the shadows and half-cover of the trees and see if he could reduce the odds any further. But he had to make his move now before the pincers of the ASU's three-pronged deployment clamped shut on him.

He estimated the distance between himself and each of his would-be assassins. The player to his right would be the last to close. He flitted from the cover of one tree to another, trying to make sure that he gave no audible warning of his direction of travel.

"Come out, fockin' Brit pig, we've got ye and yous are goin' nowhere," shouted a voice 30 yards behind him, which sounded like the unit's commander, Doyle, mouthing off. Typical.

To his left Fear heard the crack of a twig, which meant that the first man had penetrated the copse. Another burst of gunfire confirmed it, and Fear flung himself to the ground as the bullets scythed through the trees. He rolled over and took up a firing position. As he did, his Desert Boot scuffed something solid. It was a log, sawn to a length of maybe three feet, that must have been overlooked the last time a woodsman had been in there with a chainsaw. He rejected it as cover, but it got him thinking.

The situation was desperate. If all three gunmen entered the wood, the game would be over. But breaking cover and running out of it blindly would make him an easy target again. Although the depth of cover had fortunately proved greater than he'd first thought, the copse was not extensive. But if he could take out the operator who was now already within the trees he might unbolt a door that could yet let him escape. For that to be possible he would have to rely not only on his courage, discipline and shooting ability but also subterfuge.

Fear ripped off his black Barbour and threw it around the log, then picked it up. Hunching down, he carried it over to a large birch that was darkened by shade and hurriedly propped it up in a manner that might just lead a trigger-happy Provo to believe he had stumbled upon a wounded quarry.

Then he threw himself to the right of the tree and took up his position. Soon enough the crack of a clumsily broken twig tipped him the wink that he would not have long to wait to see if his ruse had worked.

"Where are ye, Fear? Bet ye never thought we'd come for you? Ya fockin' ruined ma da and noo Brit scum I'm gonne make ye pay," shouted his hunter.

Then, his eyes obviously catching the partially concealed Barbour, the PIRA spat: "Got ye."

The Provo blundered through the foliage, his bloodlust causing him to abandon any caution; his Doc Martens sent a message of approach with every footfall.

As his would-be killer drew level, Fear spat from behind the 9-milly: "Scream for me, baby," and unloaded four rounds into his target, who crumpled against a tree trunk, letting out a brief scream.

Two down, two to go. And the odds had definitely improved – not least because Fear was now in possession of an AR-18. As he rifled the corpse for anything else that could prove useful, he was delighted to find a machete hidden in the dead man's Berghaus. His armoury was building. He gave the still-warm corpse a little pat on the cheek – "Thanks, pal." – and looped it under his belt.

Looking more closely at the face, Fear wondered whether this was one of Doyle's siblings and that somehow he had affected a rapprochement with his family after the vicious job the security services had done on his reputation.

"No matter," he muttered and set about stripping off the Berghaus and putting it on himself.

For a moment a silence fell on the wood. Then it was broken by a call from the ASU's commander: "Johnny boy, you okay in there?" he shouted.

"I'm fockin' perfect, da. Just close the net and we can carve us up some Brit pig," shouted Fear, hoping the combination of the foliage and distance would make his attempt at a Northern Irish accent convincing.

As Fear knelt on one knee, he checked that the AR-18 was loaded and let his mind drift back to The Creggan and his part in the operation that had attempted to force Doyle into turning informant by planting child porn in his house and giving him the option to turn grass or face ruin, shame and being completely ostracised by his family and the nationalist community.

In the end Doyle had refused to turn and so faced the consequences of his loyalty with the discovery of the planted material. His life had been left in ruins and he was run out of Derry. Fear had often wondered what had become of the Provo zealot. Now he knew.

He failed to see the twitch of the branch to his rear, but the slight rustle of the foliage close by meant someone had crept up on him while he was reliving the past. Fear froze.

"So, ya fockin' did him, Johnny boy," said an exultant voice.

Fear thanked his lucky stars that he'd put on the purple Berghaus and the voice clearly presumed he was his mate,

Yet this unwitting subterfuge would last only as long as it took for the Provo to get 'eyes on'. Remaining in his kneeling position, Fear once again put his powers of impersonation to the test: "Beidh an la linn [the day will be with us]," he said, covering the unclipping of the machete from his belt with the sound of his words.

"Amen to that, brother," replied the Provo, stepping towards him. Judging the distance by the voice, Fear wheeled round launched the blade with all his might at the man's unprotected chest. With his gun by his side, he had no chance or responding as the glinting steel flew across the few feet between them. A look of complete shock swept over the Irishman's face as the machete slammed home, pinning him to the pine tree at his back.

His gaze dropped down, squinting at the blade and his two hands clutched at it feverishly: "Focker," he groaned, then his eyes rolled and his head fell forward.

17

THE odds were now squared, Fear realised with a rush of adrenaline. Scores that had rankled for 15 years were being settled, though not in the way his pursuers had intended. But it wasn't over yet. There was no sight of Doyle and no sound from him either, which was disconcerting. Where was he now? Could he even be looking on, lining up a last vengeful shot?

He did not have long to wait for the answer.

"That's the problem of sending boys to do a man's work, Fear," came a grating voice from the shadows, a voice that took Fear back to another lifetime.

"Drop the ArmaLite and get yer feckin' hands in the air, gobshite, then down on both knees: it's time ye met yer maker, you murderin' scum. You've taken ma boy's life, and now I will avenge Johnny and all these years of hell you put me and mine through with yer feckin' lies, Tan," hissed Doyle as he emerged from the foliage, a Widowmaker levelled at Fear.

"Well, well, if it isn't Sean Doyle, the ghost of Christmas past come back to haunt me," said Fear, keeping his face neutral.

"Shut up ta fuck! You bastard Brits cost me everything because I would'ne turn for yous, and now you've taken wan o' me ain, but at last I have you, Sergeant-feckin'-Fear," sneered Doyle.

"Come on, Sean, it was war, but it's over now, mate. Both sides did bad things, things they regret – and I regret what happened to you, Sean. Your boy…that was self-defence," said Fear, holding Doyle's blazing eyes.

"Are you serious? The boys of the old brigade may be no more, but the new lads are here to stay, and we, the soldiers of Ireland, will never give up the fight, Tan. But what yees did tae me and ma family, that wizne an act of war, it wiz feckin' personal, and there's only wan way ye can be payin' for it, Fear," Doyle growled, raising his weapon.

"So, I guess the rest of the unit are all dead and what's happened to me has left a pretty easy trail for you to follow?" Fear remarked amicably, but his eyes were searching for any possible escape route.

Doyle caught the furtive glance and smiled viciously: "Now listen, shite-in-a-bucket, seriously, what are the chances you're gonna dae anything stupid before I fill ya full of lead?"

"Pretty slim," admitted Fear, before adding: "You mind if I lower my arms before they drop off? They're getting' bleedin' heavy reachin' for the stars."

"It won't be for much longer. Okay, gobshite. So get on all fours like the animal you are. But keep yer eyes on me, 'cause I want to be lookin' in em when I riddle you full o' lead, focker. I lost it all, me wife, me kids, me place in the RA, because of the mud that stuck after yer fuckin' porno stitch up, Shraaa!"

His eyes blazing with hatred, Doyle hissed: "Now get yer hands on yer head, Brit." The moment of revenge, so long anticipated, had finally arrived. Doyle's right hand strayed from its hold on the ArmaLite to stroke the diamond stud in his right earlobe, his mounting glee clear.

It was the slip that Fear had been waiting for, and he grasped a handful of dirt from the forest floor and threw it at his tormentor's face. The earth hit Doyle's eyes, momentarily blinding him, and filled his still open mouth, making him cough and gag.

His captive launched himself at the skewered corpse still impaled on the tree, ripped the machete from his body and, turning in mid-air, launched it straight at Doyle's midriff.

But this time the blade failed to hit its mark and instead clattered off the barrel of the AR-18. Luckily, its impact was hard enough to make the spluttering Doyle drop the weapon. Fear was able to use the vital few seconds to reach the other ArmaLite before completing his roll back to a firing position.

Doyle loomed large in his sights, desperately fumbling to reclaim his killing grip on the AR-18.

"It's over, Sean, just like the war," Fear said. "Now put the shooter down and let's see if we can't get out of here alive. We've both had our lives ruined for one reason or another, but you've got to move on from the past. Eventually you've gotta let it go or what's left of your life won't be worth jack shit."

"Let it go, Brit? And can ya be tellin' me how the hell I can dae that with wan o' ma boys lying cold, feet away from you?" rasped Doyle, lowering the weapon to the ground, his breathing uneven and desperation working his features.

A snap of wood cracking close by made Fear realise that his failure to double-tap the first Provo, Doyle's son Johnny, could be coming back to bite him.

As he glanced towards the direction of the noise Doyle screamed in desperation: "Johnny…that you, lad?"

"Am feckin' comin', da," came a feral scream in reply from the behind the foliage.

Doyle, his spirit rekindled with fresh hope, desperately regained control of his AR-18 and dived for cover. It was the last move he ever made.

Fear's attention may have been distracted, but his firing finger had remained locked on the Widowmaker's trigger and he pulled it back hard.

A torrent of lethal lead shot through the air, enfilading Doyle's head, which disintegrated in a mash of brain tissue and gore. This time there was no need for a double-tap finish.

Fear retrained the AR-18 in the direction of the distraction that had so nearly cost him his life, and then he arced away to his left, hoping to take up a concealed position that would allow the badly injured Johnny to blunder into the killing ground. It didn't take long to locate him; he was staggering unsteadily through the bushes, barely able to keep a straight course.

Fear saw the unmistakeable resemblance between father and son and regretted he would have to finish the boy off if he were ever to have any peace again.

Not for the first time, the full horror of what the Troubles had done to Northern Ireland hit home, but he had to look after himself. The wounded animal was always the most dangerous, and as Johnny stumbled into the clearing where his father lay he had no time for a pang of conscience, for Johnny was still packing firepower and as the sight of his dead father hit home he let out a banshee cry: "Daaaaa!"

There was only one way this was going to end and soundlessly Fear stepped from the shadows.

The sight of his father's killer set Johnny's eyes ablaze with hatred, but raising his ArmaLite took a second too long.

The movement was telegraphed, and before the weapon had reached the ready position Fear gave him the good news with a burst of deadly lead.

The kid was blown off his feet by the power of the bullets before he was hurled onto his back, an inert bloody mass.

His corpse fell beside that of his father.

Drawing the Browning, Fear walked across the clearing and made sure, once and for all, that neither would ever raise a weapon against him again.

He walked to the edge of the small clearing, before turning back, staring at their bodies: "You've moved on, at last, focker," Ludovic Fear said aloud and then walked slowly towards the edge of the copse.

18

FEAR turned the ignition key off and, as the throaty roar of the Volumex engine died, rested his head on the leather-wrapped steering wheel with his eyes shut, letting exhaustion envelope him.

A replay of the last couple of hours rolled in his mind's eye; he knew that he'd been lucky. The remote fastness of Sheriffmuir may have been a great place for the ASU to spring their ambush, but it had also meant that the aftermath of the deadly firefight, leaving Doyle, one of his sons and the other two members of his team lying out riddled with lead, would not come to the attention of the authorities… immediately.

As dusk descended he had retraced his steps over the boggy Muir and back up to what passed for the roadway. Evidently there had been no traffic in the preceding 40 minutes, but that wouldn't last. The tractor and vehicles stood frozen in time, like a little landlocked version of the Mary Celeste.

He had repositioned the tractor in the field and ensured that the white van had been left tidily in a passing place. He hoped the Lancia hadn't been mortally wounded in the hail of bullets and was thrilled when the engine purred into life.

He had driven off in a state of shocked elation. But now sitting in the darkness outside his house, fatigue radiating throughout his body and his head pounding, reality took hold, and the horrific events rewinding on a constant loop in his head gradually ground to a halt.

What the previous hours had revealed was that he was easy to find. His would-be assassins had picked up his trail, and in dealing with them he had provided a fresh scent for the authorities that would surely lead them to his door.

The job at Dunottar Castle had been distant enough and his manipulation of the kill zone cute enough to obscure the real cause of the killings of Menzies and his crew, although The Cyclops' insistence that he be supplied with his eyeball 'trophy' could prove a fatal flaw in the picture he had attempted to paint.

What had just happened on Sheriffmuir and the identity of the deceased was likely to leave a set of questions that would only point in the direction of one man, no matter how forensically careful he had been to cover his tracks.

Fear found himself in his kitchen without recalling how he got there, staring at a glass of Macallan 12 year-old he had no recollection of pouring.

10.32 pm according to the clock and he realised he needed to clean his face and hands of the congealed blood and dirt he had only just noticed besmirched them. He yanked the kitchen tap on and splashed the ice-cold water on himself to remove the worst of the muck, before turning his attention back to the whisky.

Swirling the Macallan in his mouth he let the subtle flavours of fudge, cream and apple wash around, then made his way into the lounge and headed for the box that held his "Sinatra: The Capital Years" collection.

Fear sank back into his armchair to savour "In the Wee Small Hours", looking over the rim of the whisky glass, out through the partially open slats of the lounge blinds and into the darkness.

The bottom line was that he had so many skeletons in his past that it was likely he would spend the rest of his life looking over his shoulder and waiting for them to come back to haunt him.

Doyle, it was now clear, had more than one son, so how long would it take before the other vengeful siblings came calling?

His brain pounded at the thought; he set the Macallan down on the coffee table and ran his hands through his hair, massaging his scalp. Whisky was not the answer, but the problem was that there was no answer to his predicament.

Manipulated by The Cyclops into becoming little better than a contract killer, he was being groomed for the 'Grand Design' MacPherson had waiting for him somewhere down the line; and all the while his marriage disintegrated and a never-ending stream of phantoms formed a queue to call him to account for serving his country.

"Fuck it," Fear muttered and took a large mouthful of Macallan.

His maudlin reverie was punctured by a light rap on the front door.

The Browning that remained holstered inside the Barbour he had forgotten to shed remained reassuringly nestled under his shoulder. As he arrived at the front door force of habit took over, and Fear flattened himself against a sidewall.

Pulling the 9-milly out he flicked the safety off and pulled open the door, presenting the gun at head height.

Although her features were only half-lit by the street-light, Charlie's unmistakeable, sculpted cheekbones took on heightened definition, while her hazel eyes opened large in shock at the gun now pointed at her. Taking a step back uncertainly, her eyes flitting nervously over his taught features, she said: "Nice to see you too, Mr Fear."

Smiling awkwardly Fear reholstered the weapon, looked over her shoulders as he scanned the street, then quickly muttered an apology; "Look, I'm sorry; it's been a tough day and one that's left me a bit twitchy."

He placed his right hand on her shoulder as reassuringly as he could: "Please come in," and ushered her into the hall. He could feel the paranoia and the exhaustion of the previous few minutes evaporating, replaced by a strange sense of euphoria.

But Charlie remained in the hall, her eyes searching his face for some clue as to what led him to provide such a disconcerting 'welcome'.

"Are you sure you want me to come in?" she asked, anxiously.

"It's fine. Just what I needed. Come through," he said, indicating the open door into the lounge.

"I brought this," she said, putting a bottle on the table.

"Great. I'll get a couple of glasses."

Fear smiled, took a deep breath and looking down at the bottle of wine she had brought, smiled reassuringly: "It would be a shame to let a good Sauvignon Blanc go to waste…Charlie."

The use of her name and his attempt at humour seemed to help ease the tension, and he led her through to the lounge where Sinatra was in full angst ridden flow with "Mood Indigo".

"Make yourself comfortable and I'll find an opener for the wine," he said from behind a weak smile and bade her sit down on the large settee next to his armchair.

As he came back with the wine glasses and a corkscrew, he realised things still weren't right. "I'm sorry – I haven't offered to take your coat…" he said apologetically.

She met his gaze: "Maybe you should take your Barbour off first, Mr Fear. After all, how can you make a guest comfortable when you're not even settled in your own home?"

There was mischief in the slightly upturned corners of her mouth, and he realised that, not for the first time, he was fascinated by her lips.

Gracefully she stood up and placed the glass down, removed her navy blue raincoat to reveal a striking scarlet sequined dress that drew the eye naturally to an exquisite pair of legs. As she handed him her raincoat their fingers touched and then their eyes locked, but Fear retreated to his hallway before the moment could draw on...into he knew not what. Hanging their coats up in the cupboard he realised that he could not wait to return to the lounge...there was no point in fooling himself as to why that was the case.

He busied himself opening the wine and pouring out two generous measures. As they raised their glasses, Charlie's face broke into a smile.

Fear settled back into his chair and found that he couldn't help himself gawping at her ethereal beauty, but before the silence could draw out she smiled broadly: "You forgot to remove your...friend!" she said, pointing towards his shoulder holster.

"Jeez, sorry about that," replied Fear, slapping his forehead with his palm and quickly removing it, placing the weapon on the table.

"Are you expecting unwelcome visitors?" she asked. The smoky voice was still light, but there was a serious undertone.

"No," he said, drinking his wine and nodding in appreciation.

A puzzled look crossing her face, Charlie took a sip of wine, and he attempted to make some conversation before the silence got awkward: "Aldi, if I'm not mistaken? Pretty damn good for Kiwi Sauvy Blanc at under a fiver, if you don't mind me saying?"

As her eyes met his, the smokiness in her voice returned and she almost whispered: "I don't at all…Mr Fear."

But her eyes had taken in his dishevelled appearance, the dirt and pine needles that clung to him and the dark stain on the left breast of his navy blue shirt that were a product of his evening's work, and Charlie couldn't help her curiosity from getting the better of her: "Been a nice night for a… nature ramble, I see?"

Fear's eyes dropped down over his clothing, and he winced at the mess he was in, but tried to salvage the situation with a wan smile: "Well…I…if I'd known I was going to have such glamorous company I would have made sure I was suited and booted," he replied, which produced an answering smile.

Looking up at the Victorian fireplace, Charlie's eyes rested on a framed family photograph from a few years back. Following her gaze, Fear cleared his throat and said: "Happier times,"

"You're apart from your wife and son?" she asked, giving him a sympathetic but searching look.

There was no point in anything other than the truth: "And I only have myself to blame for it. The moral of this particular story is that if you bring shame and disgrace on your family you should never expect your wife to stand by you, especially if that includes time spent at her Majesty's pleasure," Fear said, retreating into his wine glass.

"Is that what the Sinatra is all about? 'In the Wee Small Hours' was produced when his marriage with Ava Gardner disintegrated, wasn't it?" she asked. Then, looking at the gun on the table, she said: "I hope you weren't thinking of using that on yourself, Mr Fear? Ol' Blue Eyes attempted suicide, didn't he?"

"More an attempt at grabbing attention, from what I've read. And no, that's not my style, I assure you. If anything,

I try too hard to stay alive. And…the name is Ludovic. You can even call me Ludo."

She smiled, obviously relieved. "Not an attractive man, Sinatra. But a wonderful voice, of course."

Fear, exhaustion starting to leave him increasingly flat, attempted to inject some life into his voice: "Not much regarded by people of your generation…but I'm impressed by your knowledge of Sinatra for one so…young! But then you obviously have an affinity with that era."

"Got it from dad, I guess. I seemed to be brought up with the Rat Pack."

"Talking of your dad…" Discretion deserted him: "I'm sorry, Charlie, but why are you here and, more importantly, does your daddy know?"

Her recoil at the catastrophic content of his words slapped Fear harder than any leather glove across his face ever had. Charlie jumped to her feet and slammed her wine glass down sending a wave of Sauvignon over the rim.

Her eyes blazed pure ice: "Because I thought we had a connection, Ludovic Fear; because I thought there was something different about you, something I…" But before she could finish her sentence, Fear grabbed her by the wrist and locked his lips on hers.

As Sinatra caressed the opening words of "I'll Never Be The Same" their passion and desire for each other became all-consuming.

Somewhere in the back of his mind Fear admitted to himself that never had Ol' Blue Eyes' timing never been more perfect.

But all of that could wait for another day.

19

As he opened the bedroom door Fear hovered for a moment and drank in Charlie's dishevelled beauty.

Then he walked around the bed, gently placed the orange juice on the bedside cabinet at 'her' side and felt a wave of guilt surging through him at the thought that he had done the same thing for Gina a thousand times, or more.

Charlie's blonde hair was tousled, and the smell of her was intoxicating, but the rays of weak morning sunshine that filtered through the bedroom blinds brought with them the harsh realities that now dawned with the new day.

Gently he perched himself on the edge of the bed, watched her stir as consciousness returned. The voice in his head helpfully chirped: 'So what now?'

Her delicate eyelashes started to flicker and slowly those delicious chocolate eyes opened and met his gaze, a smile parted her lips in unmistakable invitation. Fear's self-control deserted him again, and he leant down for a long drawn-out kiss before he forced himself to release her.

"Why don't you come back to bed, Ludo?" Charlie whispered mischievously, then swung the covers back to welcome him and stroked the bedsheet with long slender fingers.

"Believe me, darlin', that is the thing I want most in the world, but...we have to talk about this," said Fear, nevertheless sitting down on the bed beside her. Fear forced himself to keep his eyes on hers, telling himself it was important to keep his mounting desire under control.

Again, she surprised him by taking the initiative: "Why does there have to be a 'this'? Why can't we just enjoy it, for what it is, Ludo?"

"And what is it?" he asked, willing himself not to throw himself on top of her.

She gave him a teasing look. "Do you really have to ask? Two consenting adults doing what consenting adults do."

He inclined his head in acceptance, but unfortunately there were obvious complications, and as his right hand reached out and touched hers until their palms met and playfully pressed against each other, he knew that that there was a bottom line that must be addressed.

"What about your father? Do you think The Cyclops, er..." Fear quickly corrected himself: "Sorry, your father, is he going to be happy when he finds out?"

"Does he have to find out? Even if he does, I'm 23, this is my life to live and not his, whatever he likes to think." She felt for his hand and squeezed it.

Fear returned the pressure but continued talking: "The problem is that he's been having me watched, while he makes up his mind if he can trust me or not; and if that's still the case then he is going to know where you have been whether you decide to tell him or not."

"Right now my father isn't here, though the way you are talking about him it's beginning to feel like he is," said Charlie through a strained smile.

"He's still your father, wherever he happens to be, and being one myself I can imagine how he is going to be about this." Plus there was the not very subtle warning as to what had happened to one of Charlie's previous admirers. But he didn't want to get into that.

She was looking at him, her beautiful lips puckered in a moue of disappointment. Then she held her arms out to him.

There was no resisting her; nor did he want to. 'In for a penny…' he thought, then paused and looked into her bewitching features before continuing: "I guess if this was just a…mistake, then maybe it will go under his radar?" he concluded lamely.

Smiling wickedly Charlie suddenly sprang up from her reclining position on the bed and wrapped her arms around his neck pulling him close: "So can we make the same mistake again, Mr Fear?"

His seduction was complete, and overpowered by her sensuousness, Fear gave in to delicious inevitability.

****

Fear leaned back against the kitchen counter, cradling his coffee mug watched Charlie appreciatively as she sat cross-legged on a stool, wrapped in one of his Bengal-striped shirts, nibbling on a slice of toast.

"Do you mind me asking you a question, Ludovic?" catching him off guard.

"Feel free," said Fear, as if he didn't have a care in the world – when the opposite was the case.

"What exactly does a Security Consultant do?" Charlie asked, peering at him over her coffee mug with an apparently innocent smile.

Fear took a drink of coffee and let out a slightly weary sigh, then he parried with a question of his own: "How much do you know about your dad's business empire, Charlie?"

"More than he thinks I do. He has a lot of legitimate business interests, but I know that he is also involved in things I would rather he wasn't involved in and that he would definitely not want me to know about. I do know he has something big planned and that that's why he's hired you. Hence my question. What is it he's hired you for, Ludo?" said Charlie finishing her words in a rush.

"Leaving me out of this for a minute, how do you know what you do know about his activities?"

"Because Marty Vallance can't stop trying to hit on me and likes to think he's impressing me with some titbits that he feeds me from time to time to inflate his importance to my dad. It's mainly winks and hints, but it all points to violence and I hate it. Just like I hate the fact that you pack a gun and last night looked as though you'd been fighting a small war. Was it a small war of my father's?"

Fear was relieved to be able to answer quite truthfully: "No."

"But you have been fighting?"

'For my life, doll,' he refrained from saying.

Fear put the coffee mug down on the marbled counter surface and found his right hand filtering through his sandy mane. Thankfully, in this instance, the truth would be easier than the fiction he had thought he would need to spin.

"Something from my past. It needed sorting out..."

But before he could finish she pushed: "Your past in the SAS?"

"Yeah, I'm afraid I still have some loose ends and every so often they need to be...well, tied up, I guess," Fear said trying to give nothing away but realising that he was sounding deliberately vague and evasive.

"Loose ends that leave your clothes covered in blood and dirt and your body full of cuts and bruises, never mind the scars of the past. How many times have you been wounded in..." she stuttered, looking for the right word and this time it was Fear who interjected: "Action, I think is the word you are looking for, Charlie," adding, "Let's just say more than I would like to have."

But Charlie was not to be deflected: "These loose ends – are there anymore that might…unravel?"

Despite himself, Fear found his arms folding across his chest as his body language became defensive: "The plain truth is: yes. My problem, Charlie, is that with everything that has happened to me since I was cashiered out of The Regiment and sent down, it's easy for people from my past, who I would rather didn't know the first thing about me, to find out where I am."

She slipped off the kitchen stool and draped her arms around his neck: "All of which makes you a very dangerous man to be around, Ludovic Fear!"

Charlie stood on tiptoes and once again they kissed, but the moment was cut short by the sound of Fear's archaic ringtone.

Gently he eased her away and, groaning, said: "I better get that."

Charlie backed off, sweeping her right hand in front of her: "Who am I to come between a Security Consultant and his business, but for God's sake change that ringtone, it's…boring!"

Worries about how boring his ringtone might be was a long way down his list, especially when the caller's identity flashed across his screen: 'Cyclops.'

20

As he entered the office, Fear tried to read The Cyclops' features for a clue as to what awaited him, but from behind the steepled hands the one-eyed stare was impenetrable.

"Sit down, from what I've heard you'll be glad of the rest," MacPherson said, his words immediately setting alarm bells ringing in Fear's head.

Fear did as he was bid and The Cyclops cut straight to the chase: "What the fuck happened up on Sheriffmuir last night?" he demanded.

Fear breathed an internal sigh of relief at the direction of MacPherson's questioning and straight-batted: "Just a little unfinished business from my previous life that reared its ugly head and had to be taken care of," he replied, deadpan.

"Four dead Irishmen riddled with high velocity lead from their own automatic rifles? I'm guessing you must have pissed the Provos off big time when you were across the water…so what happened?" asked MacPherson.

"An Active Service Unit with a beef that goes back a few years decided they were going to spring a classic PIRA ambush on me. I got lucky, they didn't – simple as…" said Fear obliquely.

"Okay, I get that there's precious little you could have done about it, but how long do you think it will be before the authorities put two and two together and come knocking at your door? Sweet Christ, Fear, I can't have you being compromised by your past every time you turn a corner."

The former SAS trooper's face remained stone: "Surely you must have known that with my case being…high profile…it wasn't going to be hard for people I'd rather never set eyes on again to track me down? But if it's too much hassle for you, MacPherson, maybe we should just leave it at that and cut our losses?" MacPherson laughed: "No, my friend, you don't get out of our arrangement as easy as that. You will be released from your obligation when your work for me is complete."

"And when the fuck will that be? More to the point, can you afford to have your plans compromised, as you put it, by the baggage I'm carrying?" Fear flung back at him.

MacPherson leaned back in his chair and smiled: "I'm very lucky that the local area cop commander is a childhood friend from our days at Riverside Primary. We have a mutually beneficial arrangement, Mr Fear, which affords me certain benefits, like an early warning of trouble. But now that Central Scotland Police has been disbanded and Police Scotland established it's harder to keep things at a local level and stop them coming to the attention of Weegie arseholes with too much time on their hands, looking for a reason to justify their existence."

Fear said nothing.

"But you let me worry about all of that. What I need from you is Bancroft, by the balls. He's pissed me off once too often and now he needs to be made an example off. Bring him in, in the right frame of mind to take his medicine. Once we have taken care of him then we can turn our attention to the job I had earmarked for a man of your singular talent, all along. But we will cross that bridge when we come to it. First, you need to sort Bancroft. Have you had a chance to examine the file that Marty has compiled?"

Fear inclined his head slightly: "Yeah, everything I need to get the job done is there."

****

Lying prone concealed in the long grass on the far side of the now disused railway track that had once ferried coal from the nearby Polmaise Colliery, Fear took observations on the address he had been given in the former mining village of Fallin.

It all felt very familiar, waiting for as long as it took for the target to make his appearance. He had time to think – think back to all the similar jobs he'd done and the comrades he'd lived and worked with all those years ago.

One particular instance of cat and mouse with PIRA had provided him with a tasty solution to the Bancroft problem. It was ironic that it derived from the events all those years ago that had led Doyle to come after him. He allowed himself a grim smile.

Stirling was surrounded by former mining villages which now had problems with unemployment and, inevitably, increasing drug abuse.

Fallin had once flourished in the shadow of the Polmaise Colliery and was noted for its solidarity in the miners' strike of the 80s. It had allegedly been so strong in its support of Arthur Scargill that no pickets had been needed.

Yet three years later the strike collapsed, and the colliery had been closed, marking the end of coal mining in Stirlingshire. Mrs Thatcher's 'Enemy Within' had finally been routed, ultimately underlining the futility of the resistance.

Vallance had done his homework on Bancroft and Fear found himself wondering if the same OP who had carried out surveillance on him during the Dunottar Castle job had been involved in putting together the information on Bancroft's daily habits, hangouts and preferences, which had packed the brown manila envelope he had been given.

Fear knew that right now Bancroft would be playing darts at the local pub, The Gothenburg, while, more importantly, his missus was busy at her pole dancing class at Stirling University. There, according to the website he'd browsed, she would 'gain a massive confidence boost as you perform moves you never thought possible, while having fun and sculpting your body at the same time.'

All of which would doubtless pay dividends for Bancroft in the bedroom, but more importantly it left the lock of 27 Bannockburn Road ripe to pick.

Fear set off across the field, reaching the pathway replacing the railway track that had once seen so much coal trundled away from the colliery. He negotiated the wire fence that ran the length of the track and stood listening to the sounds of the night. Back in the Province the practice had been known as 'lurking' – lingering in the shadows, letting everyday life play out while your patrol absorbed and logged information that might initially appear of the most banal nature but, when fitted together as tiny pieces of the bigger jigsaw, would provide invaluable nuggets of knowledge.

Two doors down from the target house a shaven-headed youth was working feverishly on his motorbike inside a garage. Bright lights shone out as the sound of tools being picked up and discarded clanged through the evening air. Fear looked at his watch. Nine o'clock. How long would the pit-stop tinkering last, he wondered. He didn't have all night.

According to the file, the house abutting Bancroft's place was occupied by an octogenarian widower, and it was clear that the old boy was busy watching an episode of *Doc Martin* or whatever else was on at 9 pm on a Thursday night.

Thinking he'd just have to chance his luck with the boy racer, Fear advanced stealthily. He soundlessly whipped the wire cutters out of the rucksack and cut an opening, then slipped through it and walked down the driveway, keeping to the extra darkness of an overgrown hedgerow that ran along the side of the property.

Passing a camper van that looked like it hadn't moved from its parking place since Scargill was a boy, he skirted round the back of the house and stood for a moment peering out round the side of a small shed. No alarm system, the file had promised, so not much of a challenge – especially with an old friend from his Irish days: a universal key.

A dog a few doors down found something to bark at, but Fear was in through the back door in record time and without a sound. Once inside the house, he opened his rucksack and pulled out the magazines it contained. They needed to be carefully placed to have maximum impact, but he couldn't just leave them strewn across the coffee table. Some element of concealment was vital if Bancroft's other half was going to believe her loved one had a preference for lady boys, yet at the same time Fear had to make sure that she got the 'good' news.

Taking in the lounge, his eyes locked in on the coffee table: a two-level dark glass affair, the lower shelf of which was positively groaning with *Hello* magazines that were obviously Mrs Bancroft's staple reading.

He considered inserting the first of his 'delightful' Asian publications halfway down the pile but decided to look for a subtler marker.

Making his way upstairs, Fear entered the master bedroom. He found himself chuckling at the super-sized bed with black satin sheets beneath an extensive ceiling mirror, which indicated that Mrs Bancroft's pole dancing classes were indeed being put to good use.

At one side of the bed on a black ash cabinet a dregs-filled Celtic FC coffee mug on one of the matching bedside cabinets indicated Bancroft's side. Fear opened it and found a stack of football programmes and fanzines. Not a place Mrs B was likely to look. But judging by the immaculate tidiness throughout the house, something out of place might just draw her attention.

He selected a couple of the Thai magazines from his stash and popped them into the pile, then made sure he left the cabinet door ajar, with the corner of a couple of publications sticking out. Gina was a tidiness freak too and that would certainly have her marching over to investigate.

It wasn't much, but only a complete idiot would leave hardcore material scattered all over the house, and to do so would simply flag up that the stuff was planted. No, the wife had to believe in Bancroft's shameful perversion. Fear then slipped another magazine partially under the bed.

Next he padded his way through to the upstairs bathroom and smiled to himself as his eyes took in a pine cabinet behind which he immediately placed two more of the Thai magazines, making sure that one was partially seen from the side of the cabinet and that the other dropped down underneath into view below it.

Making his way back downstairs Fear noticed a copy of the *Celtic View* next to an armchair located nearest to the giant TV Screen that hung above the fireplace on the lounge front wall.

He shook his head ruefully as the thought struck him that he had been shoddy in his work in having failed to spot it on his first sweep through the house.

Opening the fanzine he inserted the last of the 'exotic' Oriental publications, again, slightly pulling it out from the pages that detailed the Hoops' latest saunter towards the Scottish Premiership title, then placed it back on the armchair in the type of untidy position that was sure to attract a discerning female eye.

He returned to the lounge and looked around to check nothing was out of place. On the mantelpiece, Fear noticed a holiday photo of the happy couple, smiling as though they hadn't a care in the world. Good times gone by…good times that he was about to destroy, lives he was about to ruin.

Shaking his head ruefully, Fear wrestled with his conscience, and he found himself still thinking about the photo as he made his way out of the house. It reminded him of a similar snap of himself, Gina and Monty from a holiday in Majorca, taken not so many years before. He felt a pang of guilt as he remembered that he had been due to ring Gina to arrange visiting details for his son. It was too late now.

"Shit," muttered Fear, making a vow to himself that he would make good his mistake as soon as possible and, grimacing, once again tried to place his guilt in a mental black box, visualise turning the key and leave it locked for another day.

'He's yer bleedin' son, Ludovic,' chimed the disgusted voice in his head and Fear found himself shaking outstretched hands in his frustration.

Gritting his teeth, he refocused on the photo: "For what you are about to receive may the Lord make you thoroughly grateful," said Ludovic Fear.

21

FEAR's night was by no means over. Satisfied and having subdued the pangs of guilt that had niggled him, he made his way through the village to his next port of call: The Gothenburg public house or, to be more precise, The Fallin Public House Society, handily located opposite the old Colliery.

The hostelry had been established in 1910 and had been one of several which had sprung up throughout Scotland operating a system that had been adopted from Sweden in the 1860s, which attempted to control the consumption of spirits that had proven a major problem for the Scandinavian country in the 19th century.

Now, although the colliery that had helped fund its creation had long since gone, The Gothenburg still flourished, and Fear knew Bancroft would be enjoying his usual Thursday night game of darts and a few pints with the lads, blissfully unaware of what fate had in store for him.

Fear stood on the pavement opposite and watched the smokers huddled outside, shoulders hunched as the sharp air of an autumn night warned of the season's turning.

Crossing the road he ambled up to the wall at the side of the building that encased the Polmaise Bowling Club green, and as the first of the smokers became aware of his presence Fear, his hands buried deep in his purple Moleskin jean pockets, smiled amiably: "Sorry to bother you, mate, but I've broken down just up the road towards Throsk and the AA are an hour away. Don't suppose you could spare a light?" Fear pulled a packet of Benson & Hedges from the inside of his Barbour and put a cigarette in his mouth.

"Aye, nae bother, neeber," replied a ginger-haired man, amazingly only sporting a pale blue T-shirt and denims, despite the fact he was clearly shivering, a huge Rothmans King Size dangling from his moustachioed mouth, as he squinted at Fear through a fuzz of smoke.

"Where you headed?" he asked, holding up his lighter.

Fear cupped his hand around the flame until the end of his cigarette glowed.

"Cheers. Gotta B&B in Stirling for the night, if I ever make it. Just through on a bit of business – fitting alarm systems for the football club at Forthbank Stadium in the morning," Fear said, affording himself some satisfaction from the back catalogue he'd just invented.

Fear smiled and enjoyed his fag before eventually enquiring: "Any chance of a decent pint in your shop?" He nodded at the pub, exhaling as he did.

"Aye' ye'll get a pint o' Best or a Tennent's nae bother, like. Bar'll be busy though wi' the darts just finishing off," advised Ginger helpfully.

Fear winked in acknowledgement: "Cheers, big man," he said and, taking a last drag from his smoke, stubbed it out in the ash box provided and headed through the dark wooden door into the premises of the Fallin Public House Society.

Inside was an impressive honey-coloured wooden bar that he guessed hadn't changed much since the premises had been established a century or so back. Most of it was covered by the row of drinkers who were turned round to watch the darts.

Fear attracted the attention of the barmaid, a young brunette standing with one hand placed on each of the lager and beer taps, which might have been calculated to show off her assets to best advantage.

"Pint of Best, please," he said as he eased his way towards her.

She flashed a cute smile and reached for a glass. As she poured his drink she said: "Haven't seen you round these parts before, have I?"

"Unlikely," Fear replied, adding to himself: 'not unless you've got exceptional night vision.'

"So what brings you to The Goth?" she said, putting his pint on a mat before him.

"A duff car and an hour to kill before the AA come riding to the rescue, sweetheart," said Fear, handing over a note.

"Perfect timing," the girl said, turning back from the till with his change. "'Cos in another ten minutes when the darts finishes, you'll no be able to get anywhere near the bar."

"I'm a lucky man, then," Fear said with a grin, but she was already turning to the next thirsty customer.

He consoled himself with a mouthful of his pint, and then looked at it appreciatively. A fag and a pint should set him up nicely for the second part of the evening's entertainment. Fear found himself studying a photo commemorating 'The Old Bar: 1910 to 1990' located on a wood-panelled wall and turning back to the brunette he said: "An impressive bar, nice to think that you can still have a beer in an institution that's a piece of local history." Then he took a large draft of the Belhaven and raised his pot in mock salute: "Cheers, a decent pint, needed that."

Turning his head back towards the darts match, Fear located a brown-haired man, his barnet shaven into the wood at the sides, with a ruddy complexion and narrow eyes that reminded Fear of a weasel, which was appropriate enough.

There was no doubt this was his target, from both the photo in the dossier and the holiday snap on the mantelpiece at 27 Bannockburn Road. He was standing in a small group close to the oche and seemed to be the centre of some lively banter.

"Hey, big man, shouldn't you be headin' hame? Jackie'll be back fae her pole dancin'. You don't want to be wasting any time, do you, neebs?" The speaker was a bald man with a beer belly wearing an outsize silky black darts shirt that resembled a duvet.

Almost immediately the rest of the darts players let out a raucous cheer and started mimicking the movements of a pole dancer slipping up and down her apparatus.

"Aw piss aff," shouted Bancroft, but he obviously enjoyed the attention as the ribbing was clearly driven by envy at his sexual conquest. However, he did sneak a look at the clock above the bar and sank the remains of his pint, thumping the glass down on a table, signalling that was his last of the night.

"Aye, Jimmy, you better get yersel hame if you dinnae want to miss tonight's performance," shouted one of the other players while another started howling like a dog in heat. As Bancroft headed to the door he waved his hand dismissively at his cronies but couldn't stop a smirk slipping across his sharp features.

Downing the remainder of his pint Fear turned to the barmaid: "Cheers sweetheart, good luck with the wolf pack!" he said in reference to the darts players who had continued to howl long and hard as the door had slammed behind Bancroft.

He followed Bancroft out of the pub and keeping to the shadows trailed his target down Main Street. Bancroft turned left and headed past the local convenience store en route to Bannockburn Road. But when he reached the bottom of his street, instead of turning left and heading for number 27, Bancroft crossed the road and slipped through a hole in the fence and cut down towards the rotten wooden frame of the Fallin Bridge.

Remaining in the cover of the foliage Fear kept 'eyes on' as Bancroft knelt down and started to fiddle with a polythene-wrapped package that had been secreted under one of the gnarled old stanchions.

A moment later Bancroft was bent over the railings, where he was clearly involved in a slicing and dicing operation that ended with him snorting something off a credit card through rolled up paper that looked like it was probably a tenner.

His head tilted back to the stars, Bancroft clearly enjoyed the rush of the coke and imagined the moments of pure pleasure waiting for him on his black satin sheets as Jackie treated him to his own private pole dancing performance.

Re-securing his stash underneath the old bridge, Bancroft turned and walked back along the wooden slats, a look of mounting anticipation enveloping his features.

But as he cut back down onto the bottom of Bannockburn Road a voice from the shadows rudely interrupted his fantasies.

"I'd hurry up if I was you, pal. You're not the only man who likes a bit of pole dancing. You may have missed the first showing," said Fear, his hand on his trusty Browning in his Barbour jacket pocket and his face in shadow.

"What? Who the fuck are you? What are you talking about?"

Bancroft exploded with rage. His hand slipped inside his anorak and in one fluid movement produced a blade and lunged forward. Fear had his wrist in an immediate iron grip and a moment later pressed the barrel against his victim's forehead.

"Easy, pal. Just a friendly word, tha's all...I'm Santa-bleedin'-Claus, I've just delivered me some early Chrissie presents to 27 Bannockburn Road, and in about five minutes your Missus is gonna be opening your tasty collection of exotic magazines," spat Fear from behind a vicious smile.

22

His face remaining concealed in the darkness caused by a broken bulb in the street light above him, Fear remained cautious.

Bancroft was coked up, and he was taking a chance breaking the good news to him right here, right now: "Drop the knife and get on your fuckin' knees…amigo," Fear growled in Bancroft's ear. The flick-knife hit the pavement and Fear kicked it away.

"You've been a naughty boy, Jimmy, and The Cyclops ain't happy. And now you're about to find out what happens when you cross old one eye."

Bancroft, his voice starting to quiver as he began to realise just how seriously out of his depth he was, tried to remain defiant: "Just who the fuck are you, and whit you friggin' on aboot…exotic magazines and Chrissie presents?"

Despite his defiance, Fear could sense his panic. He knew his man would keep talking, possibly incriminating himself further.

Fear kept the 9-milly pressed against Bancroft's now clammy flesh and smiled sweetly: "Now, that would be telling! Just let's say, in your case, mate, I'm the master of disaster and someone with the gift of second sight. So d'ya fancy a prediction?"

"Put that bloody gun away. I have'ne a Scooby whit yer bleetin' aboot, an' whit aw this is o'er…crossing The Cyclops? I've crossed nae wan, ken," stammered Bancroft protesting his innocence.

"Wrong answer, Jimmy son," Fear whispered close to Bancroft's ear, pushing the Browning onto his forehead and forcing him to arch his back with the pressure.

"You've been skimming, and The Cyclops has heard you've even started up your own little operation dealing seriously cut product to school kids…and that just ain't on now, is it, Jimmy Boy?"

"That's shite, I've done fuck aw," stammered Bancroft, but the voice remained shaky.

"Listen, Bancroft, I don't have any more time for your lies and neither do you, pal. You need to get home pronto to deal with your domestic situation."

He forced Bancroft back further for added emphasis.

"Listen carefully. All hell is about to break lose when your missus discovers you like to ogle rent boys and have also been subscribing to Thai magazines full of the lady boys," finished Fear.

"What the fuck have you done, you maniac?" snapped Bancroft, terror at the realisation of his impending doom enveloping him.

"You're about to get a message, and it's up to you, Jimmy Boy, if you're smart enough to understand it. If so then you'd be advised to make sure you're at the meeting."

"Whit meeting?" asked Bancroft almost before his tormentor had finished.

"Inside your *Celtic View* is a charming little magazine, and in it is a slip telling you where and when the RV is. Of course, if you don't get your arse in gear and make it back to your house pronto, your lovely lithe little lady may have found it first and then, who knows what'll happen. But I'm telling you this – if you don't turn up at the appointed time, at the appointed place, The Cyclops will take that as a declaration of war and that is something that is only gonna end one way."

Fear withdrew the Browning and yanked Bancroft upright again. For a moment the man stood staring at him in a state of shock. Then he pulled away, turned and sprinted down the street towards his front door.

Fear allowed himself a mocking laugh: "Aye, I'd fancy you against Usain Bolt mate!"

Not a bad night's work, he told himself, melting into the shadows.

23

FEAR passed the school on his left, scanning the playground for Monty as he drove by. He'd pick the boy's slight figure and unruly chestnut mop out of any crowd of kids.

He parked the Volumex a few dozen yards up the road, right after the zigzag white lines. Just as Jeremy Vine informed his Radio 2 listeners about the horrors of Lyme disease, he flicked the off switch.

Taking a deep breath he jumped out of the car and locked it. Glancing back at the Lancia, he was pleased to see that the expensive repairs necessitated by Doyle's ambush had done the trick. No one would know the car had been riddled with bullets only a day or two previously.

Blackie had done had a good job! Remembering all the ribbing he'd given the big man when Blackie had informed him his heart's desire post-regiment was to open up a garage in White Inch, Fear felt a pang of guilt.

He reached the school railings and looked into the playground trying to pick out Monty from the rest of the Riverton Primary kids who were making the most of another pleasant autumn day to enjoy their lunch break.

Just inside the fencing, at intervals of ten yards, were a series of round wooden tables, which were surrounded by groups of kids tearing into their packed lunches.

While the first two tables were occupied by smaller children wearing burgundy uniforms, the third table was swarming with bigger kids in black, and the thought struck Fear that these must be P7 kids enjoying the privilege of rank, which came with being in their final year of Primary School.

Munching on a sandwich Monty was laughing with chums when his eyes opened wide in recognition as he spotted his father. He immediately leapt to his feet, waving and running towards him.

"Dad, what are you doing here?" he gasped, gripping the fence that separated them.

"Hello, soldier," said Fear, a broad smile breaking out across his face, before he continued: "I was just passing, so thought I'd swing by and see how you were doing. I'm sorry I haven't been about, but things have been a bit difficult with my new job and…Well, you know how it is," he ended lamely, ashamed of his neglect, however inevitable it had been.

Fear shrugged awkwardly at the horrible truth he was trying to deny: 'You've been so bleedin' busy you've forgotten all about the boy,' probed the voice in his head, and he couldn't help the moisture pooling in his eyes as his fingers folded round Monty's small white paw.

He may only have been ten years-old, but his son immediately spotted his show of emotion: "What's wrong, dad, why are you so sad? Is it your new job?" Monty asked, wide-eyed.

Fear's left hand shot up to his sandy mane, and Gina's remark that this was a trademark sign of his agitation rippled through his head. Despite himself, he sighed out loud.

"Just been working long hours, mate, but I wanted to see you and let you know I will get things sorted with Mum, and maybe I can take you to your tennis or piano classes? How are you getting home from school?" asked Fear, trying to recompose himself and divert an awkward moment.

"Oh, I walk home these days, dad, it's only ten minutes, and there are a couple of other boys in the same street as me, so we all head home together. Mum has even given me my own key and I have a mobile phone as well," said Monty, smiling proudly.

Fear's eyebrows rose in surprise and he immediately fished out his Samsung: "Okie Dokie, so what's your number, and I can drop you a text and stay in touch?"

His son giggled: "Oh, em, well my mobile is in my school bag up in class and I…haven't…" he trailed off into embarrassed silence.

"Memorised the number yet?" asked Fear, smiling.

"But if you give mum a call tonight then I can tell you then," said the ten-year-old helpfully.

Fear found his hand patting his son's slight fingers: "Yeah, sure, let's do it that way. Perhaps I can also arrange to take you out for a chippie tea, maybe tomorrow?"

"Well I've got tennis tomorrow, and Ross will be giving me a lift up to the Gannochy for that, but maybe another day," said Monty smiling sweetly, unaware at the sting his innocent words had just delivered. Now he had the name of Gina's 'friend'.

Fear smiled bleakly: "Sure, mate, well I guess I better let you get back to your lunch before break is over."

Monty smiled brightly, his eyes still shining with joy at his dad's unexpected visit: "What do you think of our new black uniforms, dad? You only get to wear them when you go into P7, they're much better than the maroon and sky blue we had to wear up to P6, they were…"

But before he could finish Fear couldn't help himself applying a favourite word from his son's childhood: "Yukky!"

Monty chortled: "Daaad," he drawled out his name in mock chastisement before pointing to the tennis racket being examined by his chums back at the lunch table: "Do you like my present from your boss, it's quality…a Roger Federer tennis racket!"

Fear gritted his teeth, took another deep breath and bit back the hot words that were about to escape his mouth.

Recovering as quickly as he could he forced a smile and said evenly: "That was very kind of Mr MacPherson, your friends look jealous!"

His dad's mixed emotions had not been lost on Monty, and guiltily the boy bowed his chin onto the chest of his white polo shirt, but before he could say another word the bell rang out stridently, and Fear winced as it punctured the air.

"Saved by the bell, eh mate!" he joked and then patted Monty's hand before adding: "You better go, but tell mum I'll call her tonight, and hopefully we can get things sorted."

"Okay, dad, have a good day," said his son and leaned through the slats to shake the stooping Fear's hand in a gesture of familiar, intimate father and son affection they had shared since the morning he had taken his son to school for his first day.

As Monty turned and ran off waving, a nauseating sadness enveloped Fear; there were so many barriers between them and a new one seemed to be added every day.

Wincing, Fear pinched the tears from the corner of each eye and headed back to the Volumex, desolate.

24

HE drove in silence along through the Stirlingshire countryside, the driver's window down, as his mind replayed the implications of his meeting with Monty.

The words 'Ross will be giving me a lift up to the Gannochy' ran on a continuous loop, ramming home the reality of his situation harder with each replay.

Gina had indeed moved on. The widower from the PTA was now familiarly referred to by name and had taken his place in the everyday routine and life of his family.

He needed to stop thinking about this.

He checked the time: 2.45 pm, 15 minutes before the meeting, which was at the car park on 'Hill of Row'. He'd never heard of it, but the computer-generated American, female voice of his Google Maps oozed confidence.

The thought struck him that an obscure hill looking out over the Perthshire hills was a strange place for The Cyclops to choose as the location for his chastisement of the miscreant Bancroft.

But as he turned into the small car park the reasons behind The Cyclops' choice of this particular location became glaringly apparent. The car park was dominated by a magnificent statue of Sir David Stirling, the founder of the SAS. Fear laughed out loud. Who said master criminals didn't have a sense of humour?

A few yards away MacPherson was standing alone looking up at the great wartime leader. Exchanging a brief wave of greeting, Fear looked around and spotted Vallance waiting in the boss's green Jaguar.

As Fear climbed out his vehicle, Vallance gave a slight incline of his bald head in exchange for Fear's glance of recognition, but it was hardly a warm greeting. MacPherson, on the other, hand seemed genuinely pleased to see him, as he turned back from admiring the statue of the founder of The Regiment Fear had given his life to and which had in turn disowned him.

MacPherson was wearing his trademark black Armani suit, which seemed slightly out of place on this windswept hill. But if he felt the chill of the breeze he didn't show it.

"It's a magnificent view, and I guess the founder of your old Regiment would be happy to stand here in a place such simple beauty. He's buried down on the shores of Loch Morar," MacPherson mused.

Then his one-eyed stare levelled on Fear: "So tell me, what do you think of this impressive bronze tribute to the man who created the SAS, Mr Fear? An appropriate location for this little tête-à-tête to take place…don't you think? In the shadow of the hero who, given the fact that you are an orphan, could almost be called your surrogate father?" He paused and eyed Fear, then continued: "There was another hero of the SAS that deserves his own statue too – Sir Archie McBride. Sir David's right-hand man. Never had the fanfare he deserved, I felt. You'll have heard of him, of course?"

Fear held his gaze but refused to be drawn in: "Let's hope that Bancroft has got the message," Fear said, looking at his watch.

The Cyclops smiled benevolently at Fear's rebuff and continued with his tour guide spiel: "Did you know that there was once a circle of standing stones up here, although now all that remains are these three just over there? That magnificent pink building you can see over to the right is the House of Row, which dates back to 1480, although the original house burnt down in the 1860s. I like the pink replacement, though. What do you think?"

Fear was thinking he wished Bancroft would turn up so they could get on with their business but allowed himself a noncommittal nod.

"If Bancroft doesn't show up then I think we've got a major problem," snapped Fear, his patience being stretched by MacPherson's apparent lack of interest in the real reason behind their current location on an isolated hillside to the southeast of Doune.

"Let's just hope he did get the message before the lovely Jackie got her hands on the contents of his *Celtic View*!" said MacPherson, before barking out a harsh laugh.

He continued: "Aye, I must commend you for the imaginative way in which you made the reality of his situation clear to him. Bancroft, although you may doubt it, is not completely stupid. Greedy – yes. Ambitious – yes. Dangerous, even. But not stupid," summed up MacPherson, surprising Fear with his assessment of the man who was trying to undermine him.

While MacPherson had been talking, Fear suddenly recalled the torment of his meeting with his son, and at last the dam of his patience burst: "Do you make a habit of giving tennis-bloody-rackets to other people's children, MacPherson?"

For once the change in direction caught The Cyclops off balance, and there was a short silence while he regrouped: "A small token of my appreciation for the work his father is doing for me. Nothing more, nothing less – the delivery of which gave me great pleasure, Mr Fear. As you may recall…I am also a father and was once a dad to a small child?"

It was a cute verbal manoeuvre and one that at a single stroke put Fear on the back foot as he found himself wondering whether The Cyclops knew anything about his liaison with Charlie.

But before any reply was possible the thundering of a high-powered engine drowned out the gentle humming of the wildlife that emanated from the Perthshire hillside.

Bancroft had arrived.

25

FROM behind the steering wheel of his White Mercedes S-Class Coupé Bancroft's head could be seen glancing jerkily from Vallance, who remained perfectly still in the driver's seat of the green Jag, to Fear and The Cyclops, who stood at the foot of Stirling's impressive bronze statue.

He had come solo, which to Fear either meant he had a total disregard for his own safety or an almost suicidal confidence in his own abilities.

'Don't add up, pal,' said the voice in his head.

Within moments Bancroft was striding towards them, and as he reached the base of the monument, Fear saw that Vallance had now alighted from the Jag and was following in his wake.

Three feet away from them, Bancroft drew to a halt. His hands remaining inside the pockets of his black puffer jacket, his shoulders hunched. He said nothing, his dark eyes furtive and wary.

Fear found the experience of not knowing what was about to happen, nor having any control over whatever that would be, disconcerting. It was also contrary to all the rules of his training.

He guessed that was exactly how MacPherson wanted him to feel.

"Nice of you to grace us with your presence, James," MacPherson said by way of greeting. "Now that you're here, why don't you let us into the secret of your thought process, while we take a walk in the countryside. But first, tell me: how did your exotic magazine collection go down with Jackie?"

Bancroft's eyes narrowed to slits: "Gee us a break, Mr MacPherson. I know I fucked up, but I can make it good."

"Did you think I wouldn't find out that you were skimming, cutting the product, had started supplying high school kids with it?" demanded MacPherson.

"It was a mistake. A big wan. Stupid. I got cocky. I'm sorry," stammered Bancroft.

The Cyclops took a step forward so that his face was only inches from Bancroft's flushed features and then wrapped his left arm around his shoulders and guided him over the grass in the direction of the standing stones: "You certainly did that. Your problem, James, was that you got greedy. I could have coped with a little bit of skimming; indeed, I turned a blind eye to it initially, but then you got complacent and now you find yourself here, called to account. So tell me: was it worth it?" MacPherson pushed him away.

"Just tell me whit I can dae to make amends, Mr MacPherson?" Bancroft pleaded.

"What's in yer pockets, Jimmy? Time ye emptied them, nice an' easy, pal," commanded Vallance, who had appeared behind Bancroft without a sound.

Seeing the outline of a gun through Bancroft's clothing, Fear took over, whipping out his Browning and pressing it against his temple.

"Déjà vu, Bancroft?" he asked. "Bring it out with your fingertips on the edge of the handle, real slow…now drop it on the ground," he ordered.

Fear could feel Bancroft trembling through the barrel of his Browning and watched as a bead of sweat streaked across his furrowed brow and rolled down the side of his heavily stubbled face.

Slowly, his eyes switching nervously from MacPherson to Fear and back, Bancroft did as he was bid.

"Bravo," said The Cyclops, bringing his hands together in mock applause before he continued: "Thank you, Chief Security Officer," and beamed at Fear. Then he turned his gaze on Bancroft: "What were you thinking of doing with that?" He shook his head: "Keep walking," he added, indicating the standing stones.

Fear picked up the discarded firearm, while Vallance took up a position just behind Bancroft. He had produced his own weapon – a 45 revolver.

"Move, shitebag," he snarled, jabbing the barrel into Bancroft's back.

The short sharp bursts of Bancroft's breathing increasing in volume with every step, they made their way over to the ancient boulders.

"On your knees, James," MacPherson said when they got there. There was a tired, almost paternal sorrow in his tone.

Bancroft did as he was bid, his features overrun with terror. He had gambled and lost, and now he was about to pay for his failure.

Reaching inside his jacket pocket MacPherson pulled out a Makarov PM, flicked the safety off and paused, letting a deafening silence prevail.

"So, have you anything you'd like to share with us before you depart this mortal coil?" he asked, his dark eye fixing Bancroft with an unwavering stare.

"Fuck you, wan eye," spat Bancroft in a surprising show of final defiance.

MacPherson's head now inclined towards Fear, and turning the Makarov round he offered it to him to handle first: "Mr Fear, if you please…the pleasure is all yours."

Fear couldn't help his eyes opening wide as surprise engulfed his face.

So here it was, the ultimate test of his loyalty to The Cyclops. Execute Bancroft and there was no doubt that would be the final rite of passage – with Vallance there to witness, it would prove his admission to the inner sanctum of MacPherson's trusted confederates.

But however unsavoury a character Bancroft was and how unacceptable his actions, this was cold-blooded murder… pure and simple.

The killing of Menzies and his cohorts had been one thing, but Bancroft was now an unarmed combatant, and no rules of Close-Quarter Battle could square shooting him at close range.

"What's wrong, Mr Fear, a case of stage fright? Surely not?" taunted MacPherson. "I'm not asking you to do anything you haven't done before, am I?" He waved the gun handle to and fro waiting for Fear to take it.

Answering that question would be complicated and suggest weakness. Fear grimaced. The reality of his situation was the safety of his son and even Gina for that matter, weighed more heavily on any scales of justice than the life of a scumbag like Bancroft, who one way or another had a bullet with his name waiting for him somewhere down the line.

Fear grabbed the Makarov. He was about to commit murder, there was no other way to sugar coat it. But then he stopped. What other options might there be?

Fear knew there was only one answer.

"Go on, soldier boy, fuckin' dae him. Christ, you must have done this a hundred times over the water?" snapped Vallance from behind him.

He levelled the Makarov at Bancroft's head, and the condemned man's eyes brimmed with a mixture of defiance and desperation, but, as his final moment arrived, Bancroft lost control of his bladder, and slowly a trickle of liquid darkened his denims; yet, as his breathing rasped, he said nothing.

Fear, unable to rip his gaze away from Bancroft's hopeless features, knew that they would come back to haunt him night and day.

For a second his mind returned to Baghdad and Operation Marlborough: the sight of the Iraqi exiting the building, then the look of horror on his face as the first of his Jihadi mates hit the ground dead just before Fear's own lethal projectile blew away half of his head.

'Come on, son, you know it's gotta be done,' urged his inner voice, and Fear's finger began to caress the trigger. Gritting his teeth he saw Bancroft shut his eyes. Then he pulled back.

The gun clicked, but no shot rang out, and Bancroft's eyes opened full of disbelieving fresh hope. Fear clicked again and again, but still no shot was fired.

He turned towards MacPherson, who smiled knowingly just as Bancroft made a final plea for mercy: "Sweet Christ, MacPherson, will ye no spare me noo?"

"Not a chance in hell, arse-wipe," The Cyclops replied, and behind Bancroft Vallance took two step forwards and double-tapped him at point blank range.

Bancroft toppled into the puddle of his own urine…a dead weight.

MacPherson held out his hand for the Makarov. "Well done, Mr Fear: for you, that was the ultimate test and the good news is you passed."

Disgust engulfed Fear.

Yards away Vallance dragged Bancroft's bloodied body over to the standing stones, pulled a plastic water bottle from inside his anorak pocket, doused the corpse, flicked a Zippo lighter into flame and applied it to the newly deceased. He stood back, admiring his work.

"How appropriate, given the remains of our ancient monument, that Bancroft now has his own funeral pyre!" said MacPherson, his harsh laughter echoing out over the gently swaying golden fields.

Fear shook his head but said nothing.

"Look, Fear, there is no way Bancroft could have gone unpunished. Let him off and I'm seen as weak, and how long before he's cutting my grass again or pointing a semi-automatic at my head, for that matter? But we must look to the future, now I know I can trust you it's time we started developing the project I have enlisted you for," said MacPherson, a rare hint of warmth seeping into his voice.

"Which is?" Fear asked.

"The definition of 'Heist' in the Cambridge Dictionary is the one I prefer: namely, a crime in which valuable things are taken illegally and often violently from a place or person," said The Cyclops, clapping Fear on the shoulder and stalking off the hillside with Vallance in his slipstream.

Behind them, his hands dug deep into the pockets of his Barbour Cincinnati Wax Jacket, Fear stared unseeing at Bancroft's burning corpse.

26

CRADLING the whisky glass in his right hand Fear looked blankly at the Victorian fireplace and wondered if he would ever get round to having it restored. On the CD player Sinatra's 1959 gig in Australia with the Red Norvo Quintet was enjoying free rein. It was Fear's favourite because it captured the bravura of the great man in full flow, in the unlikely but intimate ambience of an Aussie club.

The classic arrangements of Nelson Riddle and Billy May were given fresh vigour by the informal nature of the concert's setting, and the stripped-back accompaniment of Norvo's Quintet with pianist Bill Miller's dexterous tinkling of the ivories gave the recording an added dimension.

With Ol' Blue Eyes employing great freedom in his lyric choice, often switching and twisting entire phrases, the recording was given a raucous edge.

For a moment Fear listened even more intently as the recording's moment of unique content arrived. Just as Sinatra phrased "I've Got You Under My Skin" a female member of the audience screamed out and The Chairman of the Board cracked: "Get your hands off that broad." Fear grinned and for a minute his misery left him.

Then the sound of a bottle top being cracked open – the alert of his text messenger – perforated his brief moment of satisfaction. It was Charlie: 'Are you busy tonight? Drink Jam Jar 10pm? C xxx'.

He smiled and replied with a winking face, but before he could send it, the doorbell rang.

Looking through the frosted glass Fear saw that two dark figures were standing just outside the slate roofed porch. He cursed himself once again for not having trimmed the hedge that was blocking the glow of the streetlight. Instinctively he reached out to the coffee table for his Browning.

All he had to go on were twin shadowy outlines whose arms were obscured from view by the fact they remained tight to their torsos…never a good sign.

Were his uninvited guests armed? It was unlikely that would-be assassins would announce themselves by politely ringing a doorbell if they were toting shooters. On the other hand, it was the easiest way to get someone to open the door to you.

Probably cops, he guessed, deciding not to greet them with his own piece in his hand.

Opening the door, Fear clapped eyes on the puffy features of a middle-aged man wearing a comfortable navy suit and a world-weary expression, while his second visitor was a good bit younger – maybe in his early 30s – and similarly uniformed in a dark two-piece, which confirmed Fear's supposition. It was that long-awaited visit from Her Majesty's Constabulary.

"Good evening, Mr Fear, can we have a little chat?" asked the older man, a shard of moonlight glistening off his bald head; but the two shrewd dark eyes that were switching over Fear's features warned him that this was an individual whom he could not afford to take lightly.

The ex-soldier smiled evenly: "Yeah, once you provide some identification, gents."

Almost before the words were out of Fear's mouth he had produced a small black wallet and flashed a white plastic identification card in a manoeuvre that his younger, dark-haired colleague repeated.

The two officers were in the hall in seconds, and Fear could only shut the front door after them and indicate the way to the lounge.

"I didn't see the name on your I.D.," Fear said as he followed them through.

"Detective Chief Inspector David Rothwell and Detective Sergeant Ricky Jenkins, Police Scotland," the senior officer said unapologetically.

"Thank you, Detective Chief Inspector. Be my guest," replied Fear, immediately chastising himself for the sprinkling of sarcasm he had failed to obliterate from his invitation.

Fear immediately made his way over to the CD player and gave Sinatra the rest of the night off. As he did so, Rothwell's deep, almost rumbling voice broke into life: "If you don't mind me saying so, Mr Fear, Frank Sinatra isn't the preferred listening I would expect from a man of your…er…background."

Fear turned round and gestured to his inquisitor to take a seat, smiled amiably: "As the saying goes, you shouldn't always judge a book by its cover."

The two detectives sat opposite him as the lounge became temporarily enveloped in an awkward silence. Then the younger of the two cops spoke: "Nice place you have here, Mr Fear. What made you choose to settle in Stirling?"

Irritation sprang across Fear's face before he could suppress it. Recovering himself, he failed to keep the edge from his reply: "I would have thought that was obvious: I need to be close to my wife and son, but I'm presuming you know that already DS…sorry what was your name again?"

he asked, again aware that he was betraying the non-confrontational doctrine of his training.

The younger detective gave a tight smiled before answering curtly: "Jenkins," and Fear noticed his fingers drumming on his trouser knees before he turned his attention to Rothwell.

"So how can I help you, Detective Chief Inspector?" he asked in a monotone.

"You can start by telling me all about the firefight up on Sheriffmuir that left four former PIRA terrorists riddled full of lead," DCI Rothwell said levelly.

"A nasty business, judging by the media coverage. Quite a shootout. But beyond what I've read and seen on the TV, I know nothing about it. Was there anything else?"

Fear locked eyes with the DCI, his cornflower-blue eyes bright with innocent enquiry.

"Let's stick with the 'shootout', as you characterise it. An interesting but barely believable answer given my investigations into the now-deceased PIRA commander, Sean Doyle. I believe you knew him...I find your denial of involvement hard to take seriously. How many people do you think we have running about Stirlingshire who are capable of taking out a highly trained PIRA unit single-handedly?"

"Single-handedly? How can you know that for sure?"

"It probably wasn't part of your SAS training, but you have heard of forensics, Mr Fear. The absence of dabs is annoying but five sets of prints from five items of footwear. Four very dead bodies. The maths is not complicated."

Fear kept his features neutral: "Granted. But that doesn't mean I was the one inflicting the damage, does it? Your 'line of inquiry' is purely circumstantial."

Fear settled comfortably into his armchair, quietly congratulating himself on getting rid of the sturdy walking shoes he had been wearing on that fateful day.

A tremor of irritation creased Rothwell's smooth, but still fresh features, which were at odds with a follicle-challenged dome that, combined with the extra poundage of his over-ample girth, left Fear guessing his visitor was perhaps in his late-forties.

"But you can't deny Doyle had a reason to want to kill you, and your case was high profile enough to bring you forcefully back into his mind. How hard do you think it would have been for him, or anyone else for that matter, to track you down with malicious intent?"

"Anything is possible," replied Fear stonily.

DS Jenkins was getting in on the act and stared provocatively at Fear, a muscle tic ruffling his right cheek: "The answer to that is 'not very'," spat the DS. Seizing the opportunity to turn the heat up, his relish evident, he leaned forward so that his elbows were resting on his knees, as his two hands cradled his angular chin: "Can we cut the bullshit and get right down to business?"

"Be my guest," replied Fear.

Fear took a sip of whisky. He knew the questions were about to come thick and fast from both of his interrogators and focused as hard as he could on staying non-confrontational. He sat back and awaited their next move.

The DCI had been looking at his notebook.

"You're a man with a remarkable record. Some might say you were a veritable killing machine. It's hard to see why you were sent to HMP Barlinnie, given your history and – how shall I put it – your propensity for not losing fights? Given that history, you should have done your time in Maximum Security at Shotts, but then I guess the intervention of your local MP and that petition your wife got up helped swing opinion towards leniency. A shame that by the time you came out your wife and mother of your son had moved on."

Fear urged self-restraint. He mustn't allow himself to be goaded.

"I can see why you opted to stick around here – to be close to your son and maybe even patch things up with the wife. But a fresh start elsewhere would have been a smarter move…" Rothwell paused, his piercing gaze searching Fear's face for tell-tale signs of a reaction.

He got none.

Instead, Fear let an uncomfortable silence draw on, inviting his interrogators to continue with their line of questioning but determined to give them no help.

Jenkins took over: "Come, come, Fear, I have a theory about why you have washed up in Stirling, and it isn't anything to do with your family, is it now? Ever heard of a man called MacPherson? Or to give him his full Sunday name, Obadiah MacPherson?"

Fear struggled to try and stop a quiver of surprise breaking out over his face, his mind raced; there was no point in denying something that could easily be proven and which may already have been substantiated by Rothwell and his attack dog.

But what he said next must be pitched at exactly the right level, he had to give them something but not quite what they were looking for: "Sure, I have done a bit of security consultancy work for Mr MacPherson. He has several businesses that he has asked me to look at and upgrade their protection," he replied and smiling added: "It's something I know a bit about."

"And did you know that MacPherson is also known in criminal circles as The Cyclops?"

"I didn't know he was known in criminal circles. I know him as a legitimate businessman with legitimate interests to protect. Which I am happy to help with."

"That's what you'd like us to believe, Mr Fear, but we have reason to believe that it's simply not true. Going back to your time in The Big Hoose, you must have been aware of a low-life called Jamieson, who rules the roost in there. You must have come across him."

"I knew who he was but spent my time keeping myself to myself. I didn't want any trouble, so I didn't put my head above the parapet."

"That's not what we've heard. And we know for a fact that Jamieson and MacPherson are partners. Thick as thieves, you might say."

Fear nodded his head curtly in the affirmative: "Of course. There is no way anyone who has done a stretch in C Hall wouldn't have come across Jamieson; rub him up the wrong way and it wouldn't matter who you are, you wouldn't be leaving on your feet," he answered pragmatically.

"And the interesting thing is," Rothwell came back in, "that within a week of your release you're engaged as a quote 'Security Consultant' unquote for MacPherson, AKA The Cyclops. And by some amazing stroke of coincidence within a matter of a few days one of his main rivals is eliminated along with his crew up in the North East: pumped full of lead from a high velocity rifle with strong associations with the SAS – your old regiment, to be precise, before they got wise to your penchant for criminality. What do you say about that?"

"Interesting, yes, but I'm not sure what you're getting at. From what I read in the press that was down to a squabble with the Russian Mafia, so I'm really not too sure why you're bringing that to my door."

"Really? It looks pretty simple from our side of the coffee table. Pure and simple, Mr Fear: of course you're working for MacPherson as his trigger finger. You were set up, most probably by Jamieson, when you were inside, and now The Cyclops has you by the baws, most probably by holding your wife and bairn in his sights so's you behave yourself and do exactly what he tells you. Am I right, or am I right?"

"It's an interesting hypothesis but an inaccurate one," retorted Fear flatly.

Jenkins shook his head and laughed. "Let's try you with another one. Heard of a small-time drug dealer called Jimmy Bancroft?"

Fear raised an enquiring eyebrow.

"No?" the DS said with a disbelieving grin.

"Any reason why I should have?"

"Because he's disappeared. Word has it he'd been ripping off The Cyclops and now he's just vanished into thin air? Ring any bells with you?"

"Can't say it does," answered Fear, his gaze unflinching.

Rothwell resumed his attack: "Word on the street is that The Cyclops has recruited a new hired gun, with the expertise to take out anyone, any time, any place. All of which brings us back to you…my friend," he said through gritted teeth. Detective Sergeant Jenkins slapped his notebook down on the sofa.

The DS' right index finger shot out in Fear's direction: "You are that hired gun, aren't you, Fear? The trained killer who has tipped the balance of power in the Scottish underworld in favour of The Cyclops?"

Fear reached for the glass he had almost forgotten. He drank, then smiled thinly. "How very…melodramatic Detective Sergeant. You are way off the radar."

"Really?" Rothwell took up the baton. "I have a question for you, Fear: where do you think this is all going to end? If we're right, the evidence will be there. Just enough to convince a jury, that's all we need. And then you will certainly be going to Maximum Security – for so long it won't matter who your wee wife takes up with and how your boy grows up."

"As you say: if you're right. I happen to know you're not."

Rothwell looked enviously at the malt swirling in Fear's glass. He decided to change his tone. "Look, what happened to you can't have been easy to swallow. You claimed to have been stitched up and there's a fair chance you actually were. But you're out now; it's behind you. You're free to start over. But the way things are going, you're digging yourself a hell of a deep pit. But we can offer you a way out before it's too late."

"Please go on, I'm fascinated to find out how you're going to save me from The Cyclops," Fear replied laughing.

"Come on. You know how it works. We don't want you – you're just the monkey. We want the organ grinder. Help us nail MacPherson to the wall, and you'll walk free with the chance of a clean break and a fresh start. Maybe get your life back – your life, your family and your honour," Rothwell said, leaning back in his seat, his ace played, a warm glow now radiating from his jowly features.

"So you want me to play the grass? How very ironic," answered Fear from behind a poker face.

"I prefer to look at it as your get out of jail scot-free card. Because let's face it, you may have walked out of the Bar-L but you're now bound by far tighter chains than you ever were while you were in the pokey. Come on, man, you'd have to be on the dark side of the moon not to see this is your best chance, your only chance," said Rothwell.

Fear met his dark, assessing gaze and then smiled a thin, mirthless grimace.

"If we're going to use Pink Floyd songs to help make a point then let me tell you, Detective Chief Inspector, that your offer leaves me Comfortably Numb. Now, if you don't mind, I've had a shit day and need a hot bath and a meal, so if you and your Boy Blunder can fuck back off wherever you've come from. You know where the door is." The words had no sooner spilled from his mouth than the voice inside Fear's head was cursing him: 'For Chrissakes, what did you go and do that for?'

Jenkins sprang out of the settee and launched himself at Fear, grabbing the collar of his Barbour and dragging him onto his feet until his stubbled face was less than an inch away from Jenkins' pale features: "Fuckin' hero, my arse. You fuckin' military are all the same. Think you rule the world just because you've worn a uniform and shot people. Well, you're in Civvy Street now, and you're headin' up shit creek at a rate of knots without a paddle. From what I hear you dinne even know who your faither wiz, and it's just as well for him, cause who'd want to lay-claim to scum like you?"

"Jenkins!" Rothwell stepped between them. "That's enough. We don't want the case thrown out on grounds of intimidation, do we?"

"And what case is that?" Fear remained still, his gaze locked on Jenkins' blazing eyes.

"Don't worry, Mr Fear: there will be a case and the charge will contain several counts of murder. Now let him go, Ricky, son; there will be plenty of time and opportunity to make Mr Fear come round to our way of thinking, don't you worry." Then he smiled.

Slowly Jenkins released his grip and took a step back as his superior had bade him, but the hatred he bore for Fear still burned fiercely: "Like the boss says, your time will come," he barked.

"Really?" asked Fear, before adding almost conversationally: "Now get out."

"Happy to oblige, Mr Fear, but know this: from here on in, we will be on your tail waiting for the one slip-up that will let us put you back with all the other animals; and this time nobody will be able to spout any bullshit about injustice. You will be exposed for exactly what you are…no better than a contract killer. I give you my word, Mr Fear, we will find the evidence to prove it."

27

FEAR wallowed in his bath mulling over the events of the day and trying to dissect exactly where they left him. Accessory to murder and a grilling by the police who rightly suspected him of just that, as well as the other killings he'd done at MacPherson's bidding. He sipped another mouthful of Macallan, rolling it round his tongue as he wondered what to do. Should he tell MacPherson? After all, he had made it clear he had contacts in the police. Or should he sit on it?

Then, slowly, his mind replayed the line that had stung him the most: 'From what I hear you dinne even know who your faither wiz, and it's just as well for him, 'cause who'd want to lay-claim to scum like you?'

Jenkins was at least 50 per cent right; but what if he was, in fact, the full 100 per cent spot on? Dumped in an Adidas Sports holdall outside Stirling Royal Hospital as a mere baby, disowned by parents he had never known and until right now, right here, this moment, he'd had no wish to identify.

But for some reason the rejection at birth that had always gnawed away at him had stung most during Jenkins' cruel broadside. He submerged himself under the water and held his breath but couldn't stop the images of his fallen former comrades replaying in his mind's eye like some surreal scrapbook of the dead.

Big Frank, blown up by a PIRA bomb; Jimmy Fags, found hanged in the Hereford Barracks; Frankie the Fish, his head bust wide open like an exploding teardrop by a Taliban sniper. So how was it all going to end for Ludovic Fear?

One PIRA ASU had already failed to pay him back, but how long before another lay in wait? Fall foul of The Cyclops and what could he expect? Now Rothwell and Jenkins were lining up to turn his world to shit…all over again.

He'd almost forgotten he was holding his breath under water when the burning of his lungs forced him to come up for air, and as he did so he screamed at the top of his voice: "Christ!"

He checked his watch and saw that it was 9.35 pm and time was marching on. What about Charlie? Was he going to see her?

His mobile went off and, shaking water from his hand, he glanced at the screen. He saw the identity of the caller and felt a shiver of horror run through him: 'Gina,' said the screen.

The police interview had made him forget his call, and now Monty would be in bed. Fuck, fuck, fuck.

"Hi, Gina: I was just about to call you."

"Of course you were, and if I had a pound for every time I'd heard that one over the years Monty would be at Dollar Academy. Well done, Ludovic, your son went to bed in tears…because you let him down yet again. Basically that's the only thing we can rely on you to do, isn't it?"

Running a wet hand through his hair, Fear found himself trying to dodge for cover from heavy verbal fire: "Look, it wasn't like that, Gina; my evening meeting dragged on just a bit longer than I'd intended and with it being a school night…I'm sorry, and I promise I'll make it up to Monty, maybe I could take him tenpin bowling at the weekend, if you don't have any plans, we could all three of us go…" Fear's voice tailed off as the futility of his words and his failure to take into account the new domestic order hit home.

"Never mind all of that. What do you think you were doing turning up at the school and talking to him through the fence? How does that help anything? Monty wasn't able to concentrate all afternoon, and Mr Parker gave him a warning for looking out the window. Who do you suppose he was looking for? You just don't think about anyone other than yourself and it's always been the same, Ludovic-bloody-Fear. I curse the day I met you," raged Gina as her decibels hit max.

Worried that she was about to put the phone down, Fear tried to placate her: "I'm sorry Gina, I was driving by the school on the way to a business meet when I saw Monty, and I couldn't help myself, I just wanted to speak to him. You know how little I've seen of the wee man. I'm sorry, it was stupid and it won't happen again, I promise. Now what do you say to the bowling and maybe a meal at Frankie and Benny's afterwards?"

"I'm sorry, Ludovic, but you don't seem to get it; there is no happy families for us anymore. I'm seeing someone, and Ross and I are planning on a night out." She paused, as an idea occurred to her: "But feel free to take your son tenpin bowling. In fact, are you responsible enough to take Monty overnight, now you are settled down in Riverside?" asked Gina sarcastically.

Fear stumbled again: "Oh, right…I forgot about…er… Ross. Yeah, of course, that would be great. Could I call round for Monty at five on Saturday?"

"That works for me. But I'm warning you now, Ludovic, mess this up and that's it. I'm not having you screw things up for our son all over again," warned Gina.

"I promise you I'll be there at five on the button. If you can have an overnight bag ready that would be great," said Fear and was immediately met with a harsh peel of laughter from his estranged wife.

"Fantastic! Tips on parenting from the man who has single-handedly screwed up his family! Only Ludovic Fear could come out with something so…trite! Just be there, will you," and this time the phone went dead.

Staring at the marbled tiles opposite him Fear mumbled: "That went well."

28

FEAR jumped out of the taxi and checked his watch: 10.15 pm. 'Think she's stuck around, pal?' asked the voice in his head helpfully.

Glancing across the main street he could see a few couples who had braved a nasty whistling breeze to nestle under the external awning that covered the Jam Jar's walled outdoor seating area, which had all its heaters glowing red.

But even from 100 yards he could see the billow of her blonde hair as it was tossed this way and that by the breeze, magnificently wild and untamed.

Charlie had waited.

He crossed the road dodging an apparently endless succession of Land Rovers as he went, trying to catch her eye but unsure whether she'd seen him through the traffic.

For a moment, as he walked into the seating area, another pang of guilt left Fear feeling slightly nauseous; then Gina's parting shot replayed itself inside his head in deafening high definition and he dismissed it. He pulled the chair opposite Charlie back and sat down: "Hello."

She pushed her hair back over her head, and for a moment, before her cascading locks engulfed her once again, Charlie's hazel eyes scorched him.

She said nothing.

"Look, I'm sorry; I know I'm late, and I wouldn't have blamed you if you had walked, but…I'm real glad you didn't," Fear said, trying to make light of an unpromising situation.

"It doesn't make a girl feel very good if she's left dangling on a first date…I'm not really sure why I waited. But I guess you're here now…finally," she said icily.

Fear couldn't help his right hand slide across the table as it sought out Charlie's slender fingers. He was relieved to see that they didn't recoil when he reached them.

"A business meet ran late, and then I had a bit of a domestic blowout over Monty, with his mother." He stopped, but already the damage had been done. He had allowed his domestic mess to intrude on their first proper date. His marriage to Gina was well and truly over, but he didn't want it popping up all the time like the ghost of Banquo.

"I'm sorry. What a way to start the evening…it's just a bit of a disaster," he said, turning his head upwards and closing his eyes shut.

For a moment the only sound was that of the awning's flapping canvas.

Then Charlie spoke: "Can you stop apologising? I know you're married, I know things are rocky and I chose to make this date and chose to wait for you when you didn't show up for 20 minutes. These were all my choices. You've had quite a life, Ludovic, and I can't expect the slate to have been wiped clean just because you're out for a drink with me. I'm good with it…all…I think," she said as a fragile smile slipped across her delicate features.

Before Fear could reply and, if he was honest with himself, he wouldn't have known what to say in any case, a waitress, immaculate in a Chinese-style mandarin collar blouse and a fantastic pair of black and white dog-tooth checked cigarette-style trousers helpfully intervened: "Good evening, sir! Can I get you a drink, or will you be dining with us tonight, inside the restaurant?" She let him absorb the options, a polite smile established on her impressively high cheek-boned face.

"Yes, thanks. A cold beer to start."

"Moretti, sir?"

"Perfect, thank you! What about you, Charlie?" he asked deferentially.

"Another glass of pink Prosecco would go down very nicely, thank you," she said in those smoky Bourbon tones that were already starting to work their magic on Fear once more.

He smiled at the waitress and nodded his head in gratitude before returning his gaze to the beauty that sat opposite him. God knows why she had waited but thank God she had. He felt a different man, for once happy to be who and where he was.

Her velvet voice tugged him from his reflections: "So how are you getting on…working for my dad?" asked Charlie.

He smiled awkwardly: "I think it would be fair to say that we are still getting to know each other. Your dad has a very black and white view of how things should be…"

"You mean he's right and everyone else is wrong? My father has a very strong sense of certainty…Lud-o-vic," she drawled out his name, while giving him a teasing stare.

Strangely, as Billy Joel's "Innocent Man" filled the air, his attention became focused on the black biker's jacket Charlie was wearing: "Nice leathers," he said.

"I used to be a rock chick before I became a child of the 60s. What about you? Is there another string to your musical bow or is it all about Frank and his Rat Pack?"

"So, you're a bit of a chameleon then! Well…during my spell reclining at Her Majesty's pleasure I kinda lost touch with the music scene, but – and I guess I'm showing my age – I've always had a soft spot for Deep Purple. You see, I love the sound of the Holy Trinity of keyboards, guitar and bass; and when you get someone like Coverdale or Gillan giving it the full vocal Monty, it just hits the mark for me. Although AC/DC when Bon Scott was the main man weren't bad either and Bowie…well I guess he's the ultimate chameleon…is "Life On Mars" the greatest pop song ever written…maybe," mused Fear.

As the waitress set their drinks on the table, Fear reached for the Moretti and necked the beer. He suddenly seemed to have developed quite a thirst.

He noticed Charlie's smile.

Placing the bottle back down on the table he saw her eyes sparkling with amusement: "Thirsty?" asked Charlie.

"Sorry – you've not even raised your glass. They didn't teach much etiquette in the army. Please forgive me – it's a while since I've been in civilised company, especially company as glamorous as yours…Charlie."

She laughed coquettishly: "I'm no mathematician, but I'd say that was the third apology you've made in the first 30 minutes of our date. One more will mean a yellow card!" she joked, and as they both laughed in unison their eyes locked.

Recovering himself with the help of another swig of beer, he attempted to apply a veneer of civility over his wolfish intent: "How about you, Charlie: what does a 23-year-old ex-rock chick listen to these days?"

He watched in fascination as her fingers slipped up and down her prosecco glass. Tossing her slightly curled locks back over her shoulder she said: "Ever heard of the Dark Star Riders?"

Fear shrugged before he admitted the bleedin' obvious: "Nope," and once again they both burst into peels of simultaneous laughter.

Within minutes they had made their way inside and were seated at a candlelit table situated just inside the front window, next to a roaring fire that gave off the wonderful aromatic scent of crackling logs.

"Do you want to go straight to the mains?" asked Charlie helpfully.

Fear smiled: "I'm taking it you've eaten here before; what would you recommend?" he asked putting her on the spot with a voracious grin.

She looked at him for a moment, took another sip from her wine glass and replied: "I reckon you're a steak man, no?"

"You're smart as well as beautiful!" Fear replied, but before he could attempt to get the waitresses' attention she had already materialised at his shoulder: "Would you like to see the wine menu, sir?" she asked.

"Nope, if you've got a bottle of decent Argentine Malbec that would do very nicely. If that's okay with you, Charlie?" asked Fear, once again cursing his lack of forethought.

Charlie exchanged glances with the waitress before nodding her agreement and the waitress glided away to get the wine.

"I like a man who takes charge. I'm used to it, I suppose," Charlie said smiling.

But the smile suddenly changed into a frown of what looked like horror. Fear was still struggling to turn round in his seat to see what she had seen over her shoulder, when his own heart sank.

He heard a familiar voice saying: "Hello, my dear. And this must be my Chief of Security. Good evening, Mr Fear. An unexpected pleasure. Please don't get up."

Fear felt The Cyclops' firm grip on his shoulder.

****

MacPherson walked round the table to give his daughter a kiss. Fear could see her body stiffen and she got clumsily to her feet. From across the table she looked so full of tension that he wondered if it would snap.

Then her father pulled out a chair and sat down: "How very cosy! So, in the words of the song 'how long has this been going on'?" he asked, looking from one to the other from behind a smile that dripped with barely suppressed rage.

Silence reigned, but Fear decided that it was not an option. Pumping his face into what he hoped was a confident smile, he said: "Charlie's a big girl, Mr MacPherson, as well as a beautiful one. Surely a man of the world like yourself wouldn't begrudge her a dinner date from time to time? Can I get you a glass of red?"

MacPherson looked at him and then said: "Well, if she isn't safe with my Chief of Security, who is she safe with." But his laugh sounded hollow.

"I hope he's looking after you, my dear," he said to Charlie. "At least he's ordered the wine," he added, as the bottle was brought to the table.

"Put it down, pet, and get us another glass," he said to the waitress, pouring wine for Charlie.

"Sorry," he said in mock apology to Fear: "I should have left that to you. Old habits, you know!"

The third wineglass appeared. MacPherson pushed the bottle to Fear to do the honours.

"So," MacPherson said when they all had wine in their glasses: "A toast – to surprises."

Following The Cyclops' lead, Charlie and Fear raised their glasses and mumbled "Surprises" and drank.

MacPherson put his glass down firmly and then turned to his daughter.

"Well?" he snapped.

All the sophistication and poise that previously had Fear impaled seemed to melt away as she shifted in her chair awkwardly, a little girl once more, being chastised for some piece of mischief by the man who would always be her father.

"It's our first date…I'm 23, dad. It's my business who I see," said Charlie, mustering a show of unconvincing defiance.

"But it's not the first time you've spent an evening together…is it my darling, daughter?" MacPherson's face was unreadable granite and his tone was bitter.

Turning his head, he addressed Fear.

"Does the lovely Gina know that you're taking out a young lady who is 15 years your junior, when your marriage is at such a…delicate stage?"

With a slither of a smile playing at the corner of his mouth Fear replied: "I'm afraid Gina is already in another relationship, and it's serious. Serious enough for her new partner to take my boy to tennis – equipped with his tennis racket. So really my relationship with Charlie is neither here nor there to her. Look, MacPherson, I understand this is maybe a tough one for you to…swallow, but Charlie and I have a lot in common, your daughter is beautiful, she's great company and it was Charlie who invited me out. We're living in the 21st century; but sorry, should I have asked for your permission?"

Before MacPherson could reply, Charlie beat him to the verbal punch: "If you don't mind, both of you, I'm actually here, and I have an opinion and you're both going to hear it, whether you like it or not. I'm not a child, dad, and you can't keep on pretending that I am. I know all about Ludo's domestic situation, and he's been brutally honest about it. It's up to me whether I want to spend time with him, and I've made my choice. As he said – it was me who invited him out this evening. I just want to have some fun with someone

I like and enjoy dinner with a man who isn't out for one thing. If that's okay with you…father?"

MacPherson looked at his daughter for a moment before turning his stare onto Fear: "And what are you out for, Ludo?" he demanded.

Fear inclined his head slightly: "Someone whose company I can enjoy, someone who can bring a bit of relaxation into what I'd have to say is currently a rather stressful life."

MacPherson took another sip of the Malbec, eyeing Fear over the rim of the glass before turning his gaze towards his daughter. Then he spoke: "Look, Charlie, I'm sorry if I've been…well…over-protective, but with your mother long dead it's been me and you for so long that sometimes I forget I have to let you make your own mistakes. It's just that on the fringes of my world the type of people who you come in contact with, are, well, not the type I want anywhere near my daughter."

He stopped and took a deep breath before turning his attention to Fear: "Okay, so I don't include you in the above category. You're here to keep an eye on the lowlife that hangs around The Medusa – and keep them away from Charlie. I suppose taking her to dinner is one way of doing that. But I'm warning you right now: however useful you are to me, if you mess with my daughter I will ensure that your worst nightmares are nothing compared with what I'll have in store for you. That's no empty threat: it's a statement of fact. Are we clear on that?"

Fear held his gaze for several seconds and then replied: "Crystal."

Then MacPherson drained his glass, smiled as though the previous conversation had been about something as simple as the destination of the latest family holiday and reached over to squeeze Charlie's arm.

The he stood up: "Well, I guess it's time for me to go. Enjoy your evening."

Fear, shaking his head in disbelief at the exchange, quickly pushed his chair back: "Excuse me, Charlie, I'll be back in a minute," he said, before following in The Cyclops' wake.

"I need a quick word before you go, there's something you need to know," Fear said when he caught up with him.

The eyebrow above MacPherson's one good eye raised: "Yes?" he asked.

"Outside would be best," Fear replied, pushing the door open and ushering MacPherson to an empty corner of the outdoor seating area.

"Look, I didn't want to say anything in front of Charlie, but I was paid a visit by the cops earlier tonight. A Detective Chief Inspector Rothwell and a prick of a DS by the name of Jenkins. Either of them mean anything to you?" asked Fear.

"I know of Rothwell. An ambitious career copper who's playing the politics of Police Scotland's post-amalgamation meltdown smartly enough to further himself. I guess Jenkins is his pit bull, bag-carrier and general yes-man? Probably thinks he will get a leg-up with his boss. What were they after?"

"They had me down for pretty much every violent crime that's occurred since I started with you."

"Well you weren't settling old scores with PIRA on my behalf – but they had your name on the other two, did they?"

"That's about right. I tried to fob them off, but they have started putting two and two together between the Menzies job up North, my little run-in with my old friends from PIRA and Bancroft's disappearance; and all roads are starting to lead to me."

"But they didn't have a warrant or caution you?"

Fear shook his head.

"So he's come round to shake you down. Nothing more than a fishing trip."

"Maybe...but things got a bit heated before they left, and if they didn't have it in for me before, they certainly do now," admitted Fear.

"But needless to say, you kept your cool. You're a good man, Fear – even though I'm not sure you're good enough for my daughter."

MacPherson's good eye lanced him with excoriating intensity: "Have the boys in blue rattled you, Mr Fear?" he asked, smiling viciously.

"Nope, I just thought you should know and…" Fear paused for a moment before pointing his index finger past MacPherson's shoulders: "Looks like they meant what they said."

Turning round MacPherson saw a dark blue Ford Focus parked across the street just outside Rana's Indian Restaurant, and in it the bald dome of the driver inclined forward, reflecting the light of a streetlamp. He gave them a little wave.

"Meet Detective Chief Inspector David Rothwell," Fear said without enthusiasm. "He will be pleased to see us together."

"So he mentioned me?" MacPherson asked sharply.

"Oh yes. Seemed to think I'd been nobbled inside by Jamieson." The two men exchanged a glance. "I gave him the line about being your security guy, but – well, as you can see, that hasn't got rid of him."

"And that must be his sidekick Jenkins in the back with the camera." The passenger window of the Focus eased down, and from behind a zoom lens Jenkins leaned out, before clearly firing off a stream of shots.

"Say cheese for our friends, Ludo. And then you'd better get back to Charlie. You can't keep a young girl waiting." With that The Cyclops raised a hand towards the Ford and walked on nonchalantly to his Jaguar.

29

THE Cyclops sat behind his imposing walnut desk and looked at the photo staring back at him: a blonde, pigtailed 12-year-old girl holding the reins of her first pony with her mother's arm lovingly wrapped around her shoulders. From his single eye tears rolled down a sallow cheek. "Sweet Christ!" he shouted at the four walls of his office and cuffed the droplets away. Shaking his head with frustration he tried to force the voice in his head into silent submission, but it would not go away.

Sipping a Hendrick's gin and tonic, he savoured the taste of citrus and juniper with the subtle lingering cool finish of cucumber and rose. His index finger ran over his late wife Dominique's deliciously dark and sculptured features, and for a moment he could smell the lingering floral scent of her favourite Givenchy Amarige perfume. He would never forget the first time he had given her a bottle and explained with delight that Amarige was an anagram of her native French 'mariage'!

The pain came in agonising waves as he remembered Dominique's tortured last moments in Strathcarron Hospice and how she had insisted that he anoint her with the Amarige just before her final moments, so that when she passed she could do so with her eyes shut, believing that she had died in the bluebell-wreathed meadow where they had shared their first picnic.

"Thirteen years it'll be – November 21st. Christ, how can it still hurt so much?" and again he lifted the Hendricks to his lips and applied the liquid anaesthetic for a pain that would not be dulled. Now here he was all these years later, and he could still smell her and hear the delicious Parisian inflection of her voice.

Gritting his teeth MacPherson forced himself to concentrate on the problem that now loomed so large. How could he allow his only daughter to fall in love with a man who was no more than an imitation of himself? For it was clear to MacPherson that this was exactly what Fear was, even if Fear could not know how true it was…yet. And for now, at any rate, he needed him. There was no doubting that was the bottom line.

A rap on the office door interrupted his painful thoughts. Williams shuffled in, accompanied by the powerful physique of the brooding Vallance. He bade the two men make themselves comfortable in the seats opposite him. The Cyclops' one-eyed stare swept them both, and, as was his custom, he let the silence linger to unsettle the already fidgeting Williams even more.

Then he spoke: "We have a problem. Our new friend is starting to attract too much attention from the boys in blue." Then his gaze fell on Vallance: "Marty, I need you to set up a meet with McColl; it's time some wings were clipped."

"Nae bother, boss," replied Vallance. "Consider it done."

Then MacPherson inclined his head towards Williams: "Tell me, how far down the line are we?"

"Aye it's aw goin' just the way we want it, boss mawn. The boye that owes Jamieson the 20 grand has had his baws booted. He knows that if he does'ne come across then his debts are only gonnae take him in wan direction." Williams gestured theatrically to the floor to underline his point.

The Cyclops could not help his exasperation showing, and as his fist rammed down on his desk, Williams jumped at least an inch off his chair.

"You're not pitching a film, Williams. Just give me the facts."

"Sorry, Mr MacPherson, just as ye like it. Soes the boye is cawed Shirley, and he's ready to sing like yawn wee 40s film star o' the same name. He's intae Jamieson's bookies' shoppe in Easterhouse for 20 large, and he's got naewhere to go, ken," said Williams with a brief laugh but, not wanting to incur The Cyclops' anger a second time, quickly ploughed on: "Jamieson has had his punters pay the missus and weans a wee visit in their Gable End and had them wait just long enough until the boye Jock Shirley has come hame. Apparently he turned white as a sheet and looked like his troosers were aboot tae turn broon as shite when they welcomed him intae his midden. Aye, Weegie scum, their aw the same, ken," he concluded.

This time it was Vallance who interjected: "Weegie scum they maybees but without them this Heist is never gonna happen. So get yer heid roond that Williams and, like the boss says, stick to the feckin' short and curlies of it, for Pete's sake man."

"Apologies, Marty like, but ah forgot mesel. Awright here we goes..." Williams' furtive eyes switched from MacPherson to Vallance and back again.

At last, taking a deep breath, which somehow ended in a belch and recovering with a: "Sorry like," he cut to the chase: "So the money's comin' intae Glasgae Airport from monetary exchanges fae the military and tourists alike from bases aw aer Europe, and the beauty o' it is it's aw'n untraceable notes. It comes in wance a month on the seventh oan a British Airways bus, and it's stored in a feckin' vault in the Airport. 40 mill aw waitin for us tae kiss the Queen's heid on each feckin' note. Yous wannae know the real beauty o' it?" asked Williams, rocking back and forward in excitement at the importance of the story he was telling.

"Clearly," said MacPherson from behind the rim of his glass of Hendrick's, the exasperation that had previously almost boiled over now replaced with a look of cold assessing calculation, as Williams began to put the meat on the bones of a venture he was now finding increasingly tasty.

"Shirley knows how to get us intae the vault," Williams said, folding his arms and sitting back in his chair with a leer of triumph on his face.

Vallance was having none of it: "Yer baws!" he spat.

"Naw, Marty, it's nae ma baws that are on the line here and danglin' oot the windae. The Jamieson wan has Shirley squealing for aw he's worth, and he knows there's only wan way oot and that's tae come across for Jamieson and yersel, Mr MacPherson, boss mawn," Williams concluded with a gap-toothed grin before he touched an imaginary forelock in deference to The Cyclops.

MacPherson stroked his chin gently, stared at the immaculately polished veneer of his walnut desk.

Abruptly he looked up "Very good, Rabbie boy, and you got all this from Jamieson at your prison visit to C Hall earlier this afternoon?" he asked in a strangely whispered tone that clearly disconcerted Williams almost as much as the unusual use of his Christian name.

"I did, boss, and naebody has a clue who auld Rabbie Williams is, Mr MacPherson mawn, ken. Aye they thinks me's his great uncle like, the forged papers and the gear were great, ken. These feckin' prison warden arseholes would'ne know ye were takin' the piss if ye dressed up in a red suit wi' a white beard and came in at visitin' time wi' a big sack o'er yer shoulder, ken."

And at that all three of them burst into laughter.

30

MacPherson held his hand up to still the mirth, and slowly the room was once again becalmed.

"So what else did our old friend Mr Jamieson have to say to his Uncle Rabbie?"

Williams shifted uncomfortably, his shoulders dipping up and down like an uncertain limbo dancer who reckoned the bar had been set too high: "Aye well, boss mawn, here's the rub o' it…and…these are Jamieson's words naw mine like," stuttered Williams, clearing his throat nervously.

"Just get on with it, Williams, for crying out loud," snapped The Cyclops.

Williams shrugged: "Well – and these are his words, remember, naw mine – er, he said it's time yous got yer finger oot. Says he's done the hard work and gotte the inside mawn and noo you need tae find the way tae get us in there undetected, ken. He says if ye dinne get yer finger oot aw bets are aff!"

"Oh he does, does he?" MacPherson asked of no one in particular.

"He's gotta point, boss, how the fuck are we gonnae get intae the airport unchallenged and get the job done, never mind get back oot withoot the rossers all o'er us. We're talking' armed filth everywhere at Glasgae Airport ever since these Jihadist nutters tried to blow the place to kingdom come, and now we've gotta get in there and get oor dabs on 40 mill and scarper before they twig. Fuck's sake, boss, but if we pull this one aff it will make Brinks-MAT look like a bleedin Sunday School outin'."

"Always admired that gang. They thought big. Mind you, they went in expecting to net £3 million in cash and ended up bagging £26 million in bullion and jewellery. Probably closer to £75 million today. Definitely the crime of the century. Mind you, there's none of them left to enjoy the loot. They're all dead – the lot of them," said The Cyclops, emphasising his final words.

"Aye I'd heard that. Even one of the coppers working on the case bought it with an axe in the heid!" chipped in Vallance helpfully.

"Exactly and do you know why there has been all that death in the wake of Brinks-MAT?" asked The Cyclops.

Vallance raised an eyebrow while Williams shook his head and gnawed at fingers that were already bitten to the quick.

MacPherson smiled and carried on seamlessly: "Because none of the gang had experience of disposing of the loot they netted from the job and that in turn meant they had to recruit a criminal network of figures who had. It's said that most people who've bought gold jewellery since 1993 are wearing Brinks-MAT. But the problem with all that is that the more people you involve on a job like this means the more opportunity there is for trust to break down and petty feuds to break out that take a deadly and vicious turn because of the value of the job," concluded MacPherson.

"So what're you saying, boss?" asked Williams.

MacPherson inclined his head slightly to the left: "Simply that if this Heist is pulled off we are going to need the insurance policy that Fear provides us with, because I can guarantee you that Jamieson will try and rip us off, whether he's inside or not."

This time it was Vallance who shook his head: "But the good thing about our job is that it ain't bullion and jewellery – it's used notes that'll be untraceable. The problem is how the hell are we gonnae dae that?" He looked at MacPherson for an answer.

MacPherson met his number two's gaze with a stone-eyed stare, leant his elbows on his desk and cradled his fingers: "Do you think for one minute, Marty, that I haven't taken that into consideration?" he asked. "The only way we are going to get this Heist done is by using guile rather than brawn, and that, dear old Marty, is why you are the muscle – the bludgeon, if you will – and I am the rapier."

"The success of this job is going to be all about getting in unnoticed and in plain sight and to do that we need to become wolves in sheep's clothing," he said, as though confiding a deep secret.

His two underlings looked at each other blankly. MacPherson enjoyed their bewilderment, going on: "So how do you think we can get in and out with the loot in plain daylight, not a soul having an inkling of what is going on, even though it's happening under their very eyes?" asked MacPherson amicably.

Vallance shrugged again: "Disguise?"

"Very good, Marty, very good indeed. But the key is the quality of the disguise. What type of disguise, do you think, would give us the best chance of pulling this off, dear friends?" asked The Cyclops, the slight tremor of a smile flickering at the edges of his mouth.

"Fuck's sake, gaffer, your naw wantin' us to dress up as pigs?" asked Vallance, his face skewed with incredulity.

Before MacPherson could answer, Williams had picked up the metaphorical ball and was off and running with it: "Aye, it's brilliant, boss mawn, I knew yous wid come through wi' somethin' smart, but by Christ this tops the lotte!"

"We'll leave that for another day, one that admittedly is coming soon, but suffice to say that it is all in here," said The Cyclops, tapping his head with his index finger.

"However, before that we need to take Fear out of the firing line while we get things sorted with the cops. I'm expecting him in..." MacPherson checked his Patek Philippe before adding: "three minutes, so Williams, it's time for you to toddle off. But before you go I want two things from you..."

"Just ask boss, like," replied Williams obsequiously.

"One, you start to take a considerable interest in what our new friends in the constabulary, Messrs Rothwell & Jenkins, are up to, and see if you can't find any chinks in the defences of our modern day knights in shining armour," said MacPherson, pausing to make sure Williams took in the importance of the task.

"Nae bother, Mr MacPherson," the underling replied instantly.

The Cyclops smiled sweetly: "Second, Uncle Rabbie tells his nephew that we will be good to go by the end of the month and that if he isn't ready to fall in line with my plans, as agreed, every member of his family will end up riddled with lead." He paused for effect, seeking Williams' eyes and then holding them for several seconds.

Then almost inaudibly he said: "Do you understand me?"

"Loud and clear, boss mawn," said Williams and as The Cyclops' eye jerked towards the door he jumped up from his chair and made a sharp exit.

31

As the door shut behind Uncle Rabbie, The Cyclops turned to Vallance: "I'm afraid we have another problem, Marty. Did you know Fear has been seeing Charlie?"

"Whit?" said Vallance. "Tha's no' on, boss! You canna have that."

"That's why I'm going to be sending him away. We need some loose ends tidying up before we can set the wheels in motion, and Fear can sort them while McColl takes care of his colleagues and Williams turns over some dirt on Police Scotland's answer to The Sweeney."

Vallance's dark features surveyed his boss for a moment, and then he said: "Time to take care of the Essex team?"

But before The Cyclops had the time to answer there was a rap on the door.

"Come," said MacPherson grandiosely and in walked Fear.

As he entered, the latter's eyes quickly took in Vallance's powerful figure filling the chair to his right before MacPherson gestured to Fear to take the empty seat next to his lieutenant.

He sat down. The warmth in the recently vacated leather chair tipped him off that someone else had recently been where he now was. The sensation immediately put him on his guard.

But before Fear had even made himself comfortable, MacPherson had pushed paperwork across his gleaming desk: "I'm afraid I need you to head over to Spain, Mr Fear, where I have another issue that needs taking care of before we commence countdown to the main event," he said.

Fear eyed the plane tickets with interest: "Malaga? Interesting. Another itch that must be scratched?" he asked.

"I'm afraid so. We need to clear the decks before we turn our attention to the…the Big…" MacPherson paused to apply quotation marks with the middle fingers of either hand: "…Project. I need you to make sure that there are no distractions as we move to zero hour. I have some business interests in Porto, Banús and Marbella that have been increasingly compromised by a rival interest from London, and it's time, Mr Fear, that they were put back in their box, once and for all. However, the individual who is behind this – how shall I call it – ah yes, encroachment, is someone, much like you, Mr Fear, who has skills I need to acquire. In short while I want his confederates shown no mercy, I will need Johnny The Shark brought back to Scotland very much alive and with all his senses *virgo intacta*. If you catch my drift?"

"Johnny The Shark?" Fear repeated.

"Indeed. An enterprising young man with an eye for the main chance and family connections we are going to need shortly, for all of which I am prepared to forgive him his transgressions, while letting his associates pick up the tab," said MacPherson before continuing: "Over the last few years I have built up quite a portfolio of investments. It started with the bar and grill where my late wife Dominique loved to enjoy her favourite Lobster Thermidor when we were on holiday…" But before MacPherson could continue his voice started to strain with emotion, and, for the first time, Fear observed a vulnerability in The Cyclops he had not thought remotely possible. He struggled to keep the surprise of its betrayal from breaking across his own face.

Clearing his throat quickly behind a cupped hand, MacPherson regained his self-control and moved on: "Before I knew it I had added a club and then taken advantage of the recovery of the Spanish property market to invest significant funds in an exclusive Golf and Country Club Apartment development, Los Lagos, that had stood empty since the banks closed it down back in 2008. Everything looked rosy. Until, that is, the arrival of our cockney friends."

"And now?" asked Fear flatly.

"And now I need you to 'unleash hell', Maximus!" MacPherson pronounced, purloining the line from Russell Crowe's famous *Gladiator*.

"Just what will that entail?" Fear asked.

"You will be kept busy, put it that way. Fortunately I've received intelligence that our friends, 'The Foremen' as they like to be called, will be enjoying a tour of the Los Lagos Development where properties that should have been released solely to Puerto Banús Properties, my company, have instead been pushed their way. So you, Mr Fear, will be waiting to give them a warm Scottish welcome. Johnny The Shark will be present but will not be harmed. However, I want his main henchman, Rich or Little Richard as he is imaginatively called due to his body-building prowess and their slippery Argentine financier Diego Suarez, who is the architect of this little enterprise, taken out with surgical precision. Everything you need, including mug shots of The Foremen, and a fake passport of the very highest quality, you will find in this envelope," and at that MacPherson opened the top right-hand drawer of his desk, took out a brown manila envelope and pushed it towards Fear.

Fear looked at it but did not touch it.

"This little mission comes hard on the heels of our meeting last night. I hope the sudden haste to get me out of the country is purely coincidental." Fear leant back, leaving the envelope isolated in the no man's land on top of the desk between him and The Cyclops.

"Perhaps the timing seems that way, but the need to get this done has nothing to do with you and Charlie. As I assured you, Mr Fear, if you treat my daughter the way you should, I will have no problems with you seeing her. The sudden urgency to sort things out in Spain comes as a result of some very specific intelligence. We now know where our opponents are going to be and when, so you will have the advantage of total surprise. It will require some considerable ingenuity on your part to bring Johnny The Shark back alive, but the fake Interpol Warrant and Special Branch identification papers you will find in your little package should make life easier. You will also be exceptionally well rewarded for this task. How does £50k sound?" asked The Cyclops casually, as if he was enquiring of a six year-old if a pound coin was enough pocket money.

Fear couldn't help his eyebrows raise in an arch that Roger Moore would have been proud of: "I guess that reflects the importance you are attaching to the job."

He leant forward, picking the envelope up and stuffing it inside his jacket. "Can I ask what is going to happen with Rothwell and Jenkins while I am on this Spanish job?"

"Oh don't worry about them, Mr Fear. They will be repositioned in a way that will stop them interfering with our plans and leave them in no doubt as to their own vulnerability. Now, I assume by the fact you have placed the envelope in your jacket pocket we have an agreement?" asked The Cyclops amiably.

"We do," said Fear, before adding: "I never liked fuckin' Argentineans and you can't trust a cockney as far as you can throw him."

MacPherson gave a little glint of a smile.

"Excellent," he said, concluding the interview.

32

THE tree-lined street, dominated by the brooding terra-cotta apartments that had stood empty since the banks had foreclosed on the Santa María Golf and Country Club development, seemed eerily quiet.

It was as if time had suddenly stopped sometime around 2008; workmen's tools, abandoned on the day the banks pulled the plug, still lay rusted at the entrances of underground garages while the brilliant azure of the sea sparkled in the background.

But the silence was soon broken by the noise of a car engine that became more strident as a cream Fiat 500 climbed up the hill and pulled in at the kerb on the right-hand side of the street. As it did so a tall man, pale yellow cashmere jumper draped across his shoulders, his grey-streaked hair flying in the gentle breeze, strode down tiled steps and pulled the vehicle driver's door open in welcome: "Hello mate, what's 'appenin'?" asked the driver, laughing at the warm smile of the bigger man who now greeted him.

"Señor Johnny, welcome to Santa María. I am sure you will enjoy the tour of the development and the existing apartments that the banks are prepared to release to Malaga

Investments," replied the man on the kerbside in a heavily accented voice that betrayed his South American roots.

The driver sprang out of his seat and took the hand offered: "I bleedin' hope so, Diego, or you'd be wastin' me time, me old mucka," and the younger man administered a hearty slap on the South American's shoulders.

The slam of the door at the other side of the vehicle was quickly followed by footsteps as the other occupant of the tiny cream Fiat, a dark-haired individual with bulging biceps that suggested dedicated hours spent in the weights room, stepped up onto the pavement.

"Diego, me old china plate, how are ya?" asked the second male before administering a handshake that left the older man blanching in discomfort.

But before Diego could answer, Johnny The Shark, resplendent in a pair of navy suede Baileys, turned up canvas trousers and white Ralph Lauren V-necked T-shirt, had already hit him with another question "How many apartments you got for us, my son? I hope you ain't yankin' our chains?" Then he turned to his sidekick: "Rich, you got the list of repos that we wanna take a butchers at?"

The dark-haired male duly pulled out some paperwork from the back pocket of his black flannels: "Yea, cocker, course I have, but Diego already knows the answa to that, don't he?"

The confusion knitted across the South American's sallow skin suggested he did not, and Diego shrugged his shoulders to underline as much.

"The answa is every apartment you would normally have put that Scotch bastard MacPherson's way 'as to be comin' the way of The Foremen and that process starts 'ere, don't it, Diego, my son?" demanded Rich, aggressively.

Diego smiled with relief, but his laughter was forced "Sí, sí, señor Johnny, señor Rich, that is the case. I 'ave thee up to date leest that The Cyclops would be expecting emailed to his offices in Scotland, but before eet arrives you have thee, how you say, 'first dibs' on eet."

"Nice one," smiled Johnny, but behind his boyish, almost innocent looks there was a slight but palpable hint of menace: "Well what ya waitin' for, Diego, I'm Hank Marvin, so can we get us a move on matey?"

Diego's sickly smile flickered across his face, and he held out his right hand in front of him suggesting that the two new arrivals follow him up the orange tiled steps to the first apartment on his list.

****

500 yards away Fear drummed his fingers on the steering wheel of the hired Citroën, partially hidden by the heavily leafed branches of a tree, and watched his targets, who matched up perfectly with the snaps he'd been given.

He'd been surprised by just how fresh-faced the main players had been, but now he'd seen them in the flesh, if anything, they looked even younger.

Although the development was 90 per cent empty there were a few cars dotted up and down the street and the large swimming pool opposite his current position had a couple of loungers occupied with overweight, elderly German holidaymakers, who had obviously got in early after the Spanish bank, which was rereleasing the properties, had placed them back on the market.

Above him the beautiful azure sky was polka-dotted with candyfloss clouds while a gentle breeze stirred the foliage. Sipping his Mocha, Fear enjoyed the tranquillity of this pleasant Saturday morning, running over in his mind how he would manage the carnage he was being paid to orchestrate.

It was clear that any investment in the Los Lagos Apartments was sure to be a winner to anyone who had the cash to inject, given its elevated position looking down over the sparkling Mediterranean. With the immaculately manicured Santa María golf course in the foreground and one of the area's most exclusive promenades, Nikki Beach, also just five minutes' drive away, it was the type of holiday place he'd love to bring Monty.

"Shit." The recollection hit him like a runaway train. He was supposed to be 2,000 miles away back in Stirling and looking forward to picking his son up at 5 pm to take him tenpin bowling.

Fear battered his head off the Citroën's steering wheel: "Shit!" he repeated.

He'd opened up a window of opportunity to rebuild trust with Gina, and now he'd blown it, and that would, once and for all, prove to be the end of his hopes of building any proper relationship with Monty that would allow him to spend real quality time with him on a regular basis.

Fear pulled out his phone and flicked through his contacts till he reached Gina and punched in her number. She answered immediately in a voice that brokered her icy scepticism at what was about to come next "Ludo? Please don't tell me you're going to let him down again…"

It couldn't have started more badly, and it was only going to get worse:

"Gina, I'm really sorry, but urgent business has come up…I can't make it this afternoon. I should have called yesterday, but I had to fly to Spain at very short notice. There was a lot to do."

"Which didn't include a two-minute call to me?"

Before he could get another word in, Gina's anger poured out in a torrent: "Yeah, I've heard it all before, you're really sorry, of course you are. Spain? What the hell are you doing over there? Don't tell me you only knew about this business trip this morning? That just doesn't happen…why couldn't you have called earlier? Monty has been looking forward to the tenpin all week; he's hardly stopped chattering about it and about the trip to MacDonald's – and now who has to pick up the pieces yet again? Me, that's who. You are a selfish bastard, Ludo."

"Look, Gina, I'm sorry, really I am, but I've got to work, and I can't turn down business when it comes my way. This is a big job with good money on the line, and all of that will go towards helping make things good with Monty. I'm over here looking at property in the Puerto Banús area, and when I'm finished there may be an opportunity to invest…you could benefit from that as well, if everything goes to plan." Fear left the prospect hanging in the air to try and divert Gina's rage…to no avail.

"Are you having a laugh? Benefit from what? You mean a Spanish holiday home? Are you in cloud cuckoo land? You can forget it, because that's it. You've let Monty down once too often, and it's the last time that will happen. From now on if you want any contact with your son it will be through the lawyers," raged Gina.

"Come on, Gina, you know it's not easy for me to get a new business up and running on Civvy Street after everything that's happened, please give me a break." Fear could hear the whine in his voice and despised himself.

"No, that's it. I've had enough and so has Monty. He'll be in bits when I tell him tonight's off, I'm not having it, and don't you dare try and make one of your little impromptu visits to the school at lunchtime. This is it, Ludovic, I'm warning you, if you want any contact with your boy you get your lawyer to email mine. Now…have a nice life, Ludovic Fear, and stay out of ours for good."

The mobile went dead, and Fear was left looking helplessly at his lifeless handset.

"Gina, Gina, Gina," he repeated to himself, and for a moment his mind's eye replayed scenes from a family holiday in Dublin five years back. Monty nestled on his shoulders and then supping in jest from a pint of Guinness in the company's world-famous Gravity bar, the time in the steakhouse when the waiter had mistakenly referred to the long-haired little boy who refused to have his hair cut as "Young miss," and the three of them watching Federer versus Nadal in the greatest Wimbledon final of them all, back at their hotel.

Finding his eyes filling with moisture Fear was hit with another disastrous recollection: 'What about Charlie?' asked the voice in his head. This was turning into a nightmare. He quickly sent a text, but even as he was doing so he realised that with his unreliability, domestic issues and the age gap between them, she would inevitably soon tire of him and see that her father had been right all along.

The truth was his life was no more than a façade, an empty shell. All it had to offer was the opportunity to make the type of money that could allow him to start afresh somewhere new. Christ, he had mates who, after their time in The Regiment, had relocated to places as far-flung as Melbourne and Hong Kong. He, too, would soon have the means to take off into the big wide world and start all over again.

But first he needed to take care of The Foremen. He pulled the Smith & Wesson Model 39 from the shoulder holster inside his navy Worsted jacket and fitted the MK-3 noise suppressor.

It was time to go shark hunting.

33

LOOKING out past the palm trees, over the exquisite green sward of the Santa María course, then onto the borderless blue horizon of sea and sky, Johnny The Shark liked what he saw: "Fuckin' lovely view from this balcony, Diego. Last of the three bedrooms, you say; naah, mate, you can cross this one off your viewin' list and put a sold sign up outside. This one belongs to The Foremen, best damn view in the whole bleedin' development."

"Very good, señor Johnny, eet eez yours...of course," Diego replied obsequiously, making a note on his clipboard. The tour of the Los Lagos apartments was going even better than he'd hoped, with the two cockneys chirping like demented budgies and constantly telling each other how brilliant it all was.

"Look at the size of this lounge. Man, it's massive, nice marbled floor...like the partial glazed double doors and then..." Rich strode out onto the balcony – spreading his massive arms wide: "And then you have the best balcony in the gaffe. Must be. Perfect for barbecues, vino and whatever else tickles yer fancy, eh Johnny boy? I could see you bringing Camilla up here and showing her a good time while the sun goes down, me old son!" said Rich, laughing raucously.

"Cheeky sod, ain't ya! It's just perfek whether it's for the lads on a golfing break or ma, da and the kids. Like I say, just perfek." Johnny The Shark clamped an affectionate arm around his mate as they gazed out into a world of dreams.

Diego was waiting in the lounge, doing a few numbers on his calculator. There were a lot of noughts. He was interrupted by a knock at the door.

"I geet it," he called out, though it didn't look as though the two amigos had heard him. Probably the maintenance man with some trivial question.

****

Fear stood back and waited. He could hear footsteps approaching the other side of the heavy white door. The sound of the catch on the lock being released betrayed that it was about to be opened, and this was followed by the appearance of a burly greying man who filled the doorframe and gave him an unfriendly frown of interrogation.

"You are thee Maintenance?" asked Diego, turning on an insincere smile.

Fear couldn't help a crooked grin flicker across his own stony face. The adrenaline had kicked in, and all his domestic woes had subsided as he prepared to do what he did best...kill.

"You could say that, my friend, because I've certainly come to fix something. Sorting treacherous South Americans who think they can rip people off the minute their backs are turned is top of my list of fixes today...amigo!"

Behind his Lacoste glasses a look of puzzlement crossed Diego's furtive dark eyes: "I'm sorry...I no understand?"

His question was left hanging in the air as Fear pulled the Smith and Wesson around from behind his back, and as he brought it level with the Argentine's head he spat: "Maybe this'll help," and pumped a double-tap finish into the burly property developer.

He'd come across the Smith & Wesson fitted with the MK-22 noise suppressor, favoured by the US Navy Seals, some years ago. Indeed, it had been given the affectionate *nom de guerre* of 'the hush puppy' because it was so effective at keeping animals quiet who might otherwise betray a special ops mission.

And now Fear was going to use it to keep another kind of animal quiet for good.

He stepped over Diego's crumpled corpse as the ruby red of his vital fluids began to run across the floor and silently walked into the hall, but the thud of the burly financier's inert mass hitting the marble had echoed through the empty apartment.

Standing just inside the lounge Rich's keen ears picked up the dull sound: "What the fuck?" he spluttered, pulling his Glock from his jacket. He got no further than lifting it to shoulder height, before he too collapsed, with his brains blown.

Opposite him a look of terror crossed Johnny The Shark's callow features. Fear continued his relentless march forward, stepping over the dead weight of Rich's crumpled corpse as if it was a minor piece of domestic detritus

"I hope you don't have any silly ideas," Fear said. He was reassured by the raised hands, the look of abject terror and the silently mouthing lips.

"Sorry, we haven't been introduced. Fear," he said, pleased to note that fear was what he was generating at a very high dosage. "Now please don't tell me I've shot the wrong man," he said. And then, looking down at Rich, he sighed contentedly: "Nope, I didn't. Which means you must be Johnny The Shark!"

Johnny had backed away as far as the balcony allowed and was still struggling to speak.

"Take another step towards the balcony and it will be your last, my friend.

"What…Who?"

"Like I said, Fear – Fear by name, Fear by nature." He gave a short laugh. "I'm the man who has come to help you pay for your sins…Johnny The Shark."

"What ya on about, matey? I'm a legit businessman just out to close a property deal, I don't know what your problem is, fella, but you've got the wrong man."

"No, I don't think so, pal," Fear said, still holding the Smith & Wesson in front of him. "Let's go inside. It's a bit public out here."

Keeping his terrified eyes on the gun, The Shark edged past Fear and stepped over Rich's body. He visibly stiffened at the sight of Diego slumped against the door.

"I don't take prisoners," Fear said from close behind him. "Except, you'll be pleased to hear, in your case. Now sit down and listen up."

The cockney did as he was told, barely able to keep his eyes from the corpse on the floor.

"Don't worry about him. He's paid his dues. As has your pal on the balcony. For you it's going to be more complicated. A lot more complicated.

"But…I still don't understand…"

"Did you think The Cyclops wouldn't find out that you were ripping him off?" asked Fear.

"Look, I dunno what you're on about. Who the bleedin' hell is The Cyclops?"

"Who the bleedin' hell is The Cyclops?" Fear repeated, mimicking the cockney accent.

"I'm losing patience here, pal; and if I hadn't got strict instructions to bring you back alive, you'd be well on the way to your first flying lesson – off that balcony. Comprendy?"

There was a nervous nod.

"Right, so no more pathetic attempts to pull the wool over my eyes. You know perfectly well who The Cyclops is. What I want to know is how you thought you could possibly get away with ripping him off."

But his repeated attempts to play dumb had pushed Fear's patience too far, and he strode across the marble and grabbed Johnny by his T-shirt, rammed the S&W into the side of his head and frogmarched him back towards the third floor balcony.

Forcing his head over the terracotta balustrade, Fear leant down and whispered in Johnny's ear: "Wanna learn to fly?"

"For fuck's sake, you madman, I dunno what yous on about," pleaded Johnny.

"Okay, this is your last chance. Why are you trying to rip off The Cyclops and who is pulling the strings?" demanded Fear, and for good measure he grabbed the belt on Johnny's trousers and started to pull it upwards, forcing The Shark's body slowly over the top of the balcony.

The bird's-eye view of the tarmacadam from 150 feet seemed to do the trick: "For Christ sake, just lemme down and I'll come clean," begged Johnny The Shark, "All right, all right. I admit...it was cheeky."

"Cheeky?" Fear snapped. "You're taking him for thousands and you call that 'cheeky'? He doesn't put me on a plane from Scotland to deal with people who are 'cheeky', pal – I can tell you that for free."

Fear grabbed a head full of streaked blonde hair and yanked Johnny back from the edge, slamming him down on the terracotta balcony tiles and ramming a brogue into his chest, yet still training the S&W on the cockney's head.

The desperation in Johnny's eyes shone out, and his breathing came in short sharp raps: "Look, we fucked up, I admit it. But it wasn't my call, honest to God. I'll do anything I can to help fix this mess...anything, just name it. Just lemme be."

"Oh, I will, son, I will. Or rather, The Cyclops will. You see he needs you, or rather your expertise, for a little job that's coming up soon. So you're coming back to Scotland with me where you will be given the chance to make amends and right the wrongs you've committed out here. In addition to sparing your life, The Cyclops might even give you a share of the spoils."

"What d'ya mean?"

"You'll see. And now, my friend, we have to get ready for the return flight to the UK. I'm afraid this next bit will be uncomfortable, but then you are my prisoner."

Fear leant down and placed a knee in Johnny's chest, holstered his S&W, grabbed his wrists and bound them with black plastic ties.

"It's time you paid your respects to The Cyclops."

34

IN sullen silence Johnny The Shark found himself being propelled down the tiled steps of the apartment block. When they reached the hire car, Fear unlocked the vehicle and opened the driver's door.

"Get in and say nothing," he commanded.

A moment later Fear's granite features were parked next to Johnny in the passenger seat, and grabbing his bound wrists he quickly undid the black plastic tie: "You're going to drive us to Malaga Airport where we will get on a flight for Prestwick. You've seen how I operate, any shit and you'll pay big time. Now fuckin' drive."

Then, by way of a warning, Fear pulled out the S&W and placed it under his right thigh, pointing at his unwilling chauffeur.

His darting eyes taking in the threat, Johnny smiled sweetly at his captor: "Aah, come on, matey, I'm a lover not a fighter. You'll get no problems from me, mucka."

"Just head for the Autovía del Mediterráneo and don't think about trying any monkey business."

"Aah, you mean the A-7, mucka?" asked Johnny conversationally.

Fear glared at him but decided that a stony silence would say enough.

But Johnny was not to be deterred: "Did you know how Puerto Banús got its name?"

Fear's continued silence remained deafening.

"Thought not! It was built in 1970 by a local property developer called José Banús as a luxury marina and shopping complex, and now it has over five million visitors a year," volunteered Johnny into the quiet as he drove the Fiat over a dramatic green metallic bridge that spanned the valley between the Los Lagos development and the road that took them past the impressive two-storey whitewashed clubhouse of the Santa María Golf Club.

Abruptly his passenger's glance snapped from the dramatic drop of the ravine below and back towards Johnny: "Doesn't it bother you that I've just left two of your friends filled with lead and lying in pools of their own blood?"

"Business is business in this game. What matters to me most, matey, is that I'm here still alive and kickin'. Anyways, speaking of which, since I'm gonna be having the pleasure of your company what about tellin' me your name, pal?"

Fear had had enough, and suddenly he ripped the S&W from below his thigh and pressed the barrel against the side of Johnny's head. Watched as his captive's eyes seemed about to pop out his head.

"Did you think I was joking earlier? You know exactly what my name is. Now for the last time, shut the fuck up and just drive."

****

The nasal voice of the airport announcer informed them, in both Spanish and English, that there would be a delay of an hour before their flight to Prestwick left. Fear looked out the huge glass windows of Malaga Airport and cursed the forked lightning that illuminated the late afternoon sky. The hours on the road had taxed his patience sorely.

Relieved at his reprieve, his captive had become positively loquacious, attempting to interest Fear in a welter of local knowledge, mainly about the ups and downs of the Spanish property boom.

When they'd arrived at the airport he'd enjoyed putting the ties on Johnny again and pulling them tighter than was necessary

Sitting next to him in one of the airport lounge's uncomfortable moulded grey plastic chairs, Johnny squirmed under the raincoat that was covering his bound wrists. Spending any more time with him would take Fear close to the edge. All he wanted was to get onto the plane, get the double-dealing bastard back to The Cyclops and get to bed.

"Listen to that thunder…Jeez I neva seen a storm like this over here," the irritating cockney accent whined in his ear, making Fear want to send The Shark back to his seat like an errant schoolboy. He looked him up and down. Amazing. He'd seen two of his companions gunned down in cold blood and was now cosying up to the man who pulled the trigger. There was only one word for him, but Fear had to be satisfied with repeating it silently in his head.

Another thunderclap; more lightning.

And another whine from the Shark: "I'm friggin' freezing, matey. Give me a break and put the coat over me shoulders, will ya?" he asked.

Fear smiled benevolently: "What and let the whole world know that you're a criminal being dragged back to the UK? Just stop worrying son and you'll be good as gold."

"I'll catch meself pneumonia more like," winced Johnny throwing in a shiver for good measure.

"All you need to know is that if you do what you're told you'll get back to the UK in one piece, unlike your two buddies back in Los Lagos," replied his captor.

"Look, I'm burstin' for a slash. I haven't been since you wired my hands up. You gotta help me out here. How can I take one like this?" Johnny lifted his hands up, letting the raincoat slip off his wrists in the process, to underline his point.

"You'll do just fine. The bogs are over there. Let's go," Fear said, jerking his head in the direction of the toilets, which were 100 yards to their left.

Walking towards them he kept a tight grip on Johnny's right elbow, letting him know any attempt at escape would be futile, but as they crossed the gleaming ceramic floor an elderly cleaner crossed their paths, pushing her mop-filled cart along while mumbling her discontent at a job she clearly loathed. Fear nodded courteously, but her leathery face, sheathed in a world-weary grimace, looked like it had been years since it had last seen a smile.

Briefly she stooped to pick up a discarded plastic water bottle and muttered her anger at the miscreant who had tossed it onto the floor when a bin was less than 30 feet away. "Perezoso de mierda [lazy piece of shit]," she snapped and rubbed her back as she straightened up again and groaned: "Aaeee."

Watching her anger at the extra work she had been caused by some careless holidaymaker, Fear afforded himself a brief grin as his attention wandered.

Johnny, feeling the slight slackening of the grip on his elbow and catching the diversion of his captor's attention towards the disgruntled old woman, took his chance.

Lifting his wrists up he tossed the raincoat at Fear and made directly for the cleaner's trolley, grabbed its handlebar and, anticipating the ex-SAS operator's pursuit, slammed it into his captor's midriff just as Fear had been about to grab him.

The force of the impact propelled Fear backwards and dumped him on his backside, the air temporarily dispelled from his lungs, while the cleaner let forth with a torrent of Spanish profanity: "¡Hijo de puta [son of a whore]!" she raged, as Johnny sprinted towards the concrete sanctity of the nearest toilets.

Regaining his feet Fear was aware that the entertainment Johnny's escape had provided had now made him the centre of unwanted attention, so he picked up the raincoat and walked smartly towards the toilet's open entrance as if nothing had happened.

The problem with the urinal was that it had both an entrance and an exit, and Fear knew it was vital he made the right pick in order to avoid Johnny bolting for freedom back across the terminal and attracting the type of interest that even a top quality forged Interpol Arrest Warrant and two first class fake passports were going to make very difficult to explain.

It was a 50/50 choice, and he elected to go in through the 'Out' door, but as he entered the urinals the only person in them appeared to be a middle-aged Spaniard who was effecting a quick shave to a dark five o'clock stubble…there was no sign of Johnny The Shark.

35

A ROW of six doors shielding individual WCs seemed certain to point to the cockney's hiding place, and Fear hunkered down, making his way along the tiled floor looking for any tell-tale signs of occupancy in the way of the navy suede Baileys the Shark had been sporting.

Four doors down one of the toilets flushed, and Fear rose to his feet and quickly took up a position opposite the cubicle's door. Just as he did it swung open, and a man with a grey-streaked ponytail, heavily tattooed down each arm, walked out. A second later the door to the cubicle two past him burst open, and The Shark charged out making his way through the urinal exit, his hands somehow free from the plastic ties.

"Shit," spat the former soldier and sprinted out after him, but as he made his way into the main terminal building. Desperately turning his head left and right, he could not see Johnny, and instead a group of Norwegians, pulling sports equipment hampers and resplendent in dark blue tracksuits liveried up with the badges of Malmo FC, filled his line of vision.

The Shark was nowhere to be seen.

Fear forced himself to think logically. There was only one place that Johnny would be heading for, and as he had not been through departures, didn't have a passport or a flight ticket, his only exit strategy must be to go back out through the terminal arrival foyer.

Next to the entrance was a newspaper shop that would allow Fear some cover while he attempted to keep the doorway under surveillance, but just as he thought about making his way towards it his eye was caught by a white T-shirt located in among the dark blue of the Malmo squad. Sure enough, skulking just behind one of the giant kit hampers on the shoulders of a knot of six-foot-plus, blonde Scandinavians was The Shark.

Fear's stony gaze quickly caught Johnny's darting eyes, and the former couldn't help himself raising his right hand and using his fingers to make the gesture of a firing pistol. He broke into a casual jog, looking like just another businessman running slightly late for his flight and in a hurry to hit his departure gate in time.

Reaching the first knot of footballers Fear offered a quick: "Excuse me," as he tried to negotiate a group of three players just to the right of the hamper that was between him and the fast departing Johnny.

The Norwegians were less than impressed: "Hey, what d'you think you're doing?" protested one in heavily accented English.

Beyond the hamper Johnny eyed Fear's impending presence and started to sidle round the kit chest, but he only succeeded in banging into a stocky individual, whose over-ample girth and ruddy middle-aged features suggested he might well be the kit manager. His anger spilling over, the older man grabbed a fistful of Johnny's Ralph Lauren T-shirt, and as he did so Fear struck. Placing a proprietorial hand on his prey's shoulder he quickly pulled out his immaculate, gleaming fake white plastic Police ID card: "Excuse me sir, if you don't mind, this gentlemen is the property of Special Branch on an Interpol Arrest Warrant. I'll handle things from here-on-in."

The kit manager's eyebrows arched in amazement, and behind him the nearest group of players burst into excited chatter at the events unfolding before their eyes.

Smiling amiably Fear laughed and inclined his head in Johnny's direction: "Been a bad boy, naughty magazines, donkeys and horses!"

"Pervert!" growled the kit manager as Fear quickly yanked Johnny clear of the footballers.

"Blimey! What d'ya have to do that for, matey?" asked Johnny, the resignation that his bid for freedom was over clear in his voice.

His right arm now encircling Johnny's shoulders, Fear leaned towards his right ear: "Do you know what The Cyclops likes to do to people that double cross and piss him off?"

"Buggad if I do, matey," replied Johnny.

"He has one of their eyes scooped out with a razor blade. Now, although I have to make sure you get back to Scotland in full working order, there is nothing to stop me making sure that you're minus a 'mince pie' as you cockneys like to call them. Piss me off like that again and I have a Stanley knife in my pocket that will have you looking out through one eye for the rest of your life. Just think what kind of effect that will have on your love life. Do we have an understanding?"

"Okay, okay I get it."

****

Now it was time get to the Departure Lounge and pray the storm had relented so they could get on their plane.

"We're going through security in a minute," Fear muttered to his captive. "Just so's you know, the paperwork I have for you is rock solid, so just play along with it, all right, pal. Any funny business and you'll regret it for what would be the remainder of your seriously curtailed life. Remember what I said about…an eye for an eye. Got that?"

"Sure," The Shark murmured. But Fear wasn't convinced. Still, there was no more he could do. He knew that the security gate would provide the ultimate test of the quality of his forged documentation. Although he had scrutinised the papers at length and found them flawless, a sense of foreboding was engulfing him.

He just had to trust in The Cyclops and hope for the best. 'Who dares wins,' he reminded himself and steered the Shark towards the uniforms.

"Bueno Notches, señor. El Agente Grant, Special Branch con el criminal Johnny Ayton," and at that Fear flicked back the raincoat once again covering Johnny's wrists before quickly furnishing the dour-faced official with the Interpol Arrest Warrant, followed by his gleaming warrant card and Johnny's pristine forged passport. Fear glared sideways at Johnny with a warning glare, that silence, in this case, would be golden. His eyes wide in anticipation that his captor and his fake papers were about to be rumbled, Johnny smiled sweetly but amazingly kept schtum.

The Guardia de Seguridad scanned each document in turn, and, his heart hammering, Fear knew that his moment of truth had arrived. Negotiate the security check and he and Johnny were as good as in Scotland.

The Guardia handed the documentation back to him, but just as a massive sense of relief began to wash over Fear, the official snapped: "¿Por qué no hemos tenido ninguna información de tu llegada [Why have we had no information of your arrival]?"

Guessing but nonetheless uncertain as to the exact meaning of the question, Fear played his joker: "Apenado señor, but..." he held out a hand gesturing towards Johnny: "¡Mi amigo estado chico malo [my friend been a bad boy]!" and immediately started to run on the spot, his arms pumping and his legs coming up and down like a scene from Forest Gump.

For a moment the Guardia held Fear's gaze, and his eyes slid over to Johnny, who again chose not to chance his arm. Then, as the seconds drew out, he burst into a raucous belly laugh and slapped Fear on the back: "Está bien. You go through," handing the paperwork back to Fear the official waved him through the security check.

The ex-SAS sergeant's relief was almost overwhelming. He even felt grateful to Johnny. The departures board was still showing no activity, so as they had time on their hands, he made a snap decision.

"Fuck it, fancy a beer?" he said, nodding at the bar a few feet ahead.

The Shark was genuinely surprised but happy to think that his charm offensive had finally paid off. "Good call," he said, upping his pace.

Fear guided him towards the bar: "Dos cervezas por favor, señorita?" he managed in his halting Spanish.

Moments later they sat either side of a fake beer barrel that served as a table: "So tell me what you know about The Cyclops, Johnny?"

The Shark was deep into his litre glass, lapping like a dog. Eventually he came up for air, his lips plastered with foam.

"Cheers, mate."

"You're welcome. Now, answer the question."

"The Cyclops? Apart from the fact he's got one eye, sweet Fanny Adams. I've never met him, but I'll tell you this:

he's pissed off the people in my organisation big time. He just washed up in Marbella and started out-bidding us for property. It seems like every time something tasty comes on the market he has the wink tipped and moves in before The Foremen can get first dibs on it."

Johnny raised his glass again for another lengthy swallow of San Miguel.

"But it's not just about property, is it?" Fear urged, taking a substantial sip of his own beer.

"Na, na, matey, it's all about product, innit. The Foremen, well we dominate supply the length of the Costa del Sol, or we did until your friend The Cyclops started to muscle in a couple of years back. Things got worse when he hooked up with the fuckin' Ruskies, and it's been a bit tit-for-tat ever since."

Fear remained stone-faced: "So the question is why didn't he want you rubbed out like your mates, Johnny. What makes you so special?"

Johnny took another mouthful of cerveza, but before he could answer the sound of a bottle opener – the alert to an incoming text message on Fear's phone – fizzed off.

He fished out his Samsung from his jacket breast pocket, checked the screen. It was Charlie: 'So how is the rain in Spain? No problem. C XXX'.

A look of confusion spread across his face that drew a peel of laughter from Johnny. Fear looked up and despite himself smiled back at the cockney.

"Lemme guess…woman trouble, guv'nor?" Johnny The Shark enquired with a grin.

"You could say that," Fear said, already tapping in his reply: 'Rain + thunder, but back early tonight. Curly Coo at 9? L'.

Moments later a smiley face indicated the reply he had hoped for, and taking a draught of San Miguel he turned his attention back to The Shark: "You haven't answered my question. So what is your USP, Johnny? Why are you still here – causing me serious inconvenience?"

The Shark checked Fear's face to confirm that the question was friendly banter and then gave a conspiratorial grin.

"Word is that old one eye is planning something major, and he's been putting the feelers out lookin' for some… expertise," replied Johnny.

"So what expertise do you bring to the table, Johnny?"

"It's not me so much. More family connections. But no doubt he'll tell me himself when he sees me. But what about you, El Agente Grant, what d'ya bring to the table?" and at that a mischievous grin crept across The Shark's youthful features. Across the table Fear, despite himself found laughter escaping him.

"You, for starters. But generally? I make problems go away, Johnny."

36

The Cyclops shifted uncomfortably on the handcrafted wooden chair and looked out over the water's serene calm as the weak glow of the autumn sunlight faded fast.

The Lake of Mentieth was Scotland's only natural lake and an environmental oasis where you were as likely to see otters playing in the shallows as an osprey dive-bombing from a great height for a fish supper, while herons intermittently patrolled the lakeside.

The Lake of Mentieth Hotel had once been a manse for the nearby church, while the Priory on the Isle of Inchmahome had played host to many distinguished visitors: most notably, Mary Queen of Scots herself.

It had been a favourite of his late wife Dominique, and they had often enjoyed a leisurely Saturday lunch amid the natural beauty and the wildlife. Now other matters demanded his attention.

The recent changes in the Scottish Police Service that had seen the regional or the local forces replaced with the national Police Scotland body had proven problematic for MacPherson and hadn't helped the cosy little arrangement he had with the area's senior cop, Chief Superintendent

Jimmy McColl, a former schoolmate at Riverside Primary and lifelong friend.

With the emergence of DCI Rothwell and DS Jenkins, MacPherson's security policy did not provide the comprehensive gold-plated cover it had done, and as such MacPherson had called McColl to a meeting at which he intended to point out a few home truths that would encourage McColl into curbing the enthusiasm being shown by his two junior colleagues for delving into his business and, in particular, Fear's work.

He knew McColl would come, for the skeletons that he could help breathe life into would come marching back out of the senior detective's cupboard if he did not.

Their current relationship had proven hugely beneficial, but, as MacPherson's keen single-eyed gaze caught sight of a stooping heron, he was forced to admit it had probably now reached its defining moment.

MacPherson found a pang of sadness seep through him as the rumbling of a diesel engine and the sound of tyres on the hotel's gravel car park signified that his moments of enjoyment savouring the still beauty of the lakeside he'd once shared all those years before with Dominique, were about to be ended.

McColl got out of his car, flexed his legs, buttoned up his black Reefer coat until the collar was around his ears and then walked down onto the small grass area by the lake.

Down at the lake MacPherson strolled along the shore, thinking about the ties of friendship weighed against the demands of business and the plan he was about to put into action. Absent-mindedly, he stooped to pick up a smooth flat pebble. Then, as he had on previous, happier occasions, he flicked it across the still water and enjoyed watching its low-level skim across the lake's surface. Dominique had always enjoyed his prowess as a stone-skimmer. If only she had lived. How different would his life be now?

"Aye, you've scared the heron away; he'll naw be happy now you've cost him his supper!" said a gruff voice from a few yards behind him.

MacPherson continued to look out over the lake.

"None of us are happy if someone costs us our supper," he said, slowly turning to greet the pencil-thin McColl.

McColl's ravaged features had not changed much since a bout of childhood chicken pox had left his skin pitted, but the shrewdness of his eyes shone bright in the dimming lakeside light: "But are you sure the venture you have been planning is naw gonnae do exactly that, old friend?"

MacPherson smiled at the term of endearment: "Not if you take care that two of your over-enthusiastic colleagues stick their noses somewhere else. Coffee?"

McColl smiled, nodded in the affirmative and they both trudged up through the darkening glore and a few minutes later, with two Cappuccinos ordered, were seated at the side of a fiercely crackling log fire that brought the warmth back to their chilled bodies.

"There's nothing which has yet to be contrived by man by which so much happiness is produced as by a good inn or tavern. Dr Johnson," MacPherson read from the framed quotation on the mantelpiece.

"The man had a point, did he not, Jimmy?" asked MacPherson amicably.

McColl looked up from his coffee. "Didn't he also say that the best thing in Scotland was the road leading to England?"

MacPherson gave a short bark of a laugh. "But at least he called it as he saw it. And that, my old friend, is what I must do."

McColl smiled thinly but continued to sip on his Cappuccino and let a silence draw out as he held MacPherson's inquisitorial gaze. They had been here before, MacPherson playing his mind games and always ready to have the last word. But then, as McColl knew full well, being a copper on the take meant that he was always going to be vulnerable, no matter how far he went back with his paymaster.

"I'm sorry, Obadiah, but it's just not so simple anymore. Since we became Police Scotland my control has been eroded. Randolphfield may be the Headquarters but I'm afraid that when it comes to watching the detectives that is now out of my control," said McColl flatly.

MacPherson stretched his hands to the fire, his body thawing out nicely, undid the buttons of his overcoat and then leaned back on the comfortable oak chair: "I've been thinking about that, Jimmy, and I'm afraid we are going to have to come up with something; indeed, I'm afraid you're going to have to come up with something, regardless of the new politics playing out up at Randolphfield…that is if you want to maintain our friendship."

Although he tried to dispel it, McColl couldn't suppress the flicker of alarm that spread across his pocked face before MacPherson had spotted it: "Look, Obadiah, I know I owe you, and the last thing I want to do is go upsetting the apple-cart but…" McColl spread his arms out to underline how helpless he felt.

"What is the size of your bookies' bill, Jimmy?" asked MacPherson as he fished out a slip of paper, unfolded it and pushed it into the middle of the oak table: "Is that close?"

McColl picked up the slip with his right hand: "Shite, are you sure it's 92K?" he asked, his voice crackling with alarm at the realisation of just how bad his gambling addiction had become.

"Come, come Jimmy, you don't think my boys would fail to keep a tally? You're an honoured client. That's why you've got such a generous facility of your little…" MacPherson paused to apply quotation marks with the middle fingers of both hands: "Habit."

McColl attempted to appeal to childhood loyalties: "Come on, Oby, it has'ne all been one way. How many turns and tip-offs have you had over the years that have kept you one step ahead of the law and the local-fuckin'-competition for that matter?"

MacPherson smiled but continued to stare into the flames: "Indeed you have a point; but the main point now is that I have been planning this project for too long to let a couple of jumped up little police pricks pull the rug from under my feet and you, Jimmy, are going to help me prevent that from happening."

McColl couldn't help himself: "And tell me, Obadiah, how the fuck's that gonna happen?"

"I'm afraid you are going to help me make sure that Randolphfield's answer to Bodie and Doyle come by some information that will take them somewhere that will allow you to make them go away…for good," said MacPherson, slowly turning his one eye towards McColl and waiting for the realisation of what he was demanding

McColl's agitation was clear: "Wait a minute, you're saying you want me to send Rothwell and Jenkins somewhere for you to have them bleached? Christ…You want me to be an accessory to murder? Are you out of your fucking mind, MacPherson?" McColl's voice was a strained whisper. He looked around the bar to make sure no one was overhearing their conversation.

MacPherson also lowered his voice, but there was no loss of intensity: "No, not an accessory: I want you to be their executioner. It's the only option left on the table that works for you…and for me."

McColl was so stunned he couldn't speak. The colour drained from his face, leaving it a mask of horror.

37

FEAR pushed through the green wooden doors of The Curly Coo, congratulating himself on the fact that for once he wasn't late.

His good mood was enhanced when he saw the range of craft beers on offer. And the ambience of the place was warm and friendly. A good choice and it seemed that Madonna Black's write-up in the *Stirling Observer* had been accurate.

What had also been correct was the description of the warmth provided by the stone stove to his right and the comfort that would clearly be provided by the well-padded burgundy Chesterfield wall seating.

But his panoramic surveillance of the cosy ambience provided by the Curly Coo's interior was interrupted by the Cumbrian accent of the small but formidable dark woman behind the bar: "What you drinking, my friend?" she asked from behind the bar.

The answer was easy: "Pint of Joker, please, young lady," Fear replied with a smile.

"I've not seen you in the Coo before, have I? We'll get along much better if you drop the young lady patter."

Fear caught her flinty gaze for a moment and hoped his smile was as charming as it needed to be to appease the landlady of what could hopefully become his local.

"My apologies."

"I should think so," came the tart reply.

Her expression didn't lighten when he continued: "Oh, and I better have a glass of Prosecco as well."

The landlady acknowledged the order, unsmilingly. 'Why's she still cross with me,' Fear wondered. Then it dawned on him. No woman likes references to her years: 'Oh God, she must have thought I was dissing her for her age. Me and my big stupid gob,' he thought.

The scowl as the drinks were put down on the bar confirmed his suspicion. Fear thought about a further apology but realised that would only make things worse. Instead he silently passed a note over and scooped up the drinks.

Fear took a mouthful: "Beats the shit out of the Spanish muck I've been force-fed for the last couple of days."

The words were barely out of his mouth when the smoky, slightly husky voice, which had been tormenting him ever since he'd first heard it at The Medusa, whispered: "You made it. Glad to see you haven't forgotten all about me… Ludo,"

"Certainly did. Prosecco?"

Turning round Fear found her delicious smile waiting for him, and, despite himself, he leant forward and kissed her on the lips and then spontaneously blurted out: "Missed you."

Charlie looked at him quizzically: "Really?" she asked.

"The table next to the fire's just become free. Let's go," he said, leading the way. Having installed Charlie with her Prosecco, he went back for his change and was met with a shrewd assessing gaze of the landlady.

"Lucky man!" she said.

"So how was Spain?" Charlie asked on his return.

Fear took a mouthful of his pint. Suddenly he felt very tired. His mood had certainly taken a dive, and he couldn't blame it all on screwing it up with the landlady. "Okay," he said weakly. Then realising that that wouldn't suffice, he added: "Actually, it was bloody disastrous."

"How so? Did it go badly?"

It did for some, he thought darkly, remembering the two bodies in the apartment.

"Oh no. Got the business done. It's just that…" he said flatly and placed his pint pot down on the table with a little bit too much force.

"You messed up with Monty?" Charlie asked perceptively.

"Big time. Forgot all about the bowling and then when I called Gina on Saturday morning she went mental and told me that's it, I now need to go through my lawyers if I want access." said Fear, his left hand rifling through his shaggy hair.

"Bit messy, then? I'm sorry to hear that. Your Spanish jaunt must have been something quite important for you to have forgotten about your son…" the note of chastisement in Charlie's voice was so tantalisingly slight that Fear almost missed it…almost.

But it also triggered the intriguing thought in his head that perhaps The Cyclops' daughter knew more of her father's affairs than she had, so far, let on.

"Yeah, it was quite important, in fact I guess I'll only know how important in the weeks to come…I need to ask you a question Charlie…and I'd appreciate an honest answer."

A hint of steel glinted from her brown eyes, and Charlie took a sip from her Prosecco: "Which is?"

Fear smiled at her cute tactic of answering question with a question: "Just how much do you know about your father's work and what he has planned?"

She met his eyes squarely: "Just what I can get out of Marty Vallance."

"Which is?"

"All he said was that my father has something major on the go...something so big that Marty called it a game changer. That's all I know, I'm afraid. I'm guessing you know a lot more. Was the Spanish trip anything to do with it? It seemed to come at very short notice – you didn't even have time to square things with Gina. But you've left me wondering what the real reason for us meeting up was? You said you'd missed me when I arrived, missed me for what, the information you thought you could get out of me?"

Fear looked up at her. There was no doubt about it. He was being judged. He shrugged awkwardly and sighed. Safer than trying to talk himself out of trouble after a long and highly stressful couple of days away. He sought her chocolate-eyed gaze: "I think you know me well enough now, Charlie, that that isn't the case."

She smiled almost awkwardly at his peace offering, and he noticed that, in a girlish gesture, she slipped her hands under her knees and sat on them: "So...what exactly is it that worries you, Ludovic?" she teased coquettishly, her biker jacket collar flopping around her porcelain features.

"Take your pick: the fact there's almost 20 years between us, the fact you're The Cyclops' daughter, the fact I'm coming out of a wrecked marriage and look like I've got a nasty custody fight on my hands for my own son. Jeez... where do I start?" Fear said distractedly.

"But...if all these things are a problem then why did you want to see me so urgently tonight?" Charlie asked slyly.

Fear held her eyes from above his pint and slowly placed the glass down: "I've missed you, Charlie. I can't get you out of my head. Can't stop hearing your voice inside it, seeing your face in my mind's eye and all of that worries me..."

"Because?"

"Because, Charlie MacPherson, I'm too old and my life is too screwed up to be falling in love with someone like you."

****

She held his gaze, her face a study in frozen surprise. Then slowly a smile started to break across her exquisite features, yet still she said nothing and instead reached for the glass of Prosecco, which she sipped all the while holding his spell-bound features.

"Your life is too screwed up to be falling in love with someone like me? I'm not really sure how to take that..." she smiled mischievously.

Wrong-footed and embarrassed by the mess he'd made of things, Fear shifted uncomfortably in his seat, took a deep breath and said: "Look, I'm sorry I've made a mess of things, it was a stupid comment, but the simple truth is that no matter how much I hate what I do, how much crap I get from Gina, I see your face in my mind's eye and it...warms me to the core. An old sergeant of mine once said that 'Life's no dress rehearsal,' and he was bang on the money with that."

"But what about Gina and Monty? Don't you have to make things right with them before there can truly be an us?"

There it was again, another of her disconcerting questions hitting the nail on the head. "They're not the only players, are they?" he parried. "There's also your father, who is also a major player in any 'us', I get that, so there's no point wasting any more time and getting in any deeper...if all of that is too much."

Slowly her right hand stretched across the table, and her fingers intertwined with his, then her face lit up with the warmth of a smile that was heartbreakingly tender, and Fear knew then that he would never forget this moment.

"But I don't care about anyone else, Ludovic Fear. All that matters is you and me. Your old sergeant was right, life is no dress rehearsal, and I don't want to share mine with some boring accountant who spends his time listening to Level 42, his weekends playing golf with his chums at the club or some high-flying lawyer that has been hand-picked by my father. The moment I met you, up at The Medusa, I knew you were different...the truth is, I just don't know if I'll ever meet anyone like you again."

"Really? Is that truly how you feel?"

Fear felt an irresistible wave of joy rushing through him, forcing his mouth into an enormous smile that became a laugh of pure happiness. He looked up at Charlie, who caught his eye and burst into laughter too. It was as though a huge weight of anxiety had been lifted from his shoulders.

"I thank God for you, Charlie MacPherson...you've made me feel alive again. But you know there is going to be a rough ride ahead until we can, one day, get where we want to be?"

"I don't really care as long as I'm taking it with you, Ludovic Fear, but you must promise me one thing..." and her voice trailed off into silence.

"Which is?"

"Please make things right with Monty and Gina."

Fear stared into the fire for a moment before responding: "Believe me that's something I will never stop trying to do and..." but before he could finish his sentence she leant forward, cupped his face in her hands and kissed him.

38

"Lookin' forward to that pint, boss, before I go home for my egg and chips!" DS Jenkins said, his hands rammed deep in his overcoat as he trudged along Barnton Street, the rain stinging his face.

"On a night like this, Ricky, son, it's not just the pint that matters, it's the boozer and the warmth of a decent fire to go with it, and this place ticks all the boxes. To be fair The Curly Coo also has one of the best Malt Selections you're gonna find this side o' the Cairngorms," muttered DCI Ricky Rothwell, ripping open the door of the Curly Coo, almost charging into the warmth of the pub.

Right behind him Jenkins was quick to record his appreciation: "Aaah just what the doctor ordered. It's your round, gaffer, if memory serves? I'll try and get us a table near the stove. My suede brogues are feckin' soakin'..."

But Rothwell's focus seemed to have been diverted from the row of malts he'd been studying.

"I'd say the best table in the house is already taken... wouldn't you, Ricky, son?"

Jenkins' eyes followed his gaffer's gaze over to the coal burning stove, where Fear and Charlie, their hands entwined, only had eyes for each other.

"Eu-fucking-reka!" exclaimed Jenkins, but before he could move in their direction Rothwell's hand grabbed his arm: "Let's hit the bar first, I'm going to enjoy this all the more with a drink in hand."

Rothwell elbowed his way past a nondescript drinker, who was reading a *Daily Record* and, despite the heat from the nearby coal stove, had his black and yellow Helly Hansen zipped up full and a Beanie hat pulled down over his ears.

"Take it easy, mawn," said the barfly, before grabbing his pint of Best and vacating his previously cherished spot as Rothwell barged in: "Two pints of the Schiehallion, thanks," and then turned back to join Jenkins gazing over at the couple by the fire.

"Isn't that sweet?" he said, while the intimidating landlady pulled the pints. Jenkins grinned in anticipation at what was coming.

"You know why I like a pint of Schiehallion so much, Ricky, son?" he asked.

"No, gaffer, why would that be?" asked Jenkins in an almost pre-choreographed line that he'd used a thousand times before receiving one of his gaffer's sermons.

"Because She-hal-i-on is the type of craft lager that brings intense reward for the sort who like to plant their flag at the very top of the mountain."

Rothwell smiled benignly and then turned back to the bar where his two pints were laid smoothly on the counter by the small dark lady with the features that had 'don't mess' written all over her...but the DCI did not heed their warning.

"Cheers, doll," he smiled, picked up the beers and began to turn away.

"That'll be six fifty, my friend," said the landlady in her hybrid mix of English northern accents that seemed to point to an upbringing around the Lakes, perhaps Lancashire maybe even both.

Rothwell eyed Jenkins and jerked his head back towards the bar: "Pay her, will you, Ricky, son."

But as Jenkins forked out his cash the landlady spoke again: "By the way, friend, I'm no your sweetheart or your doll."

Rothwell turned back and held her gaze; his jaw setting, he said nothing. He had bigger fish to fry, and turning he made his way over to Fear and Charlie.

Reaching their table, he slapped the pint of Schiehallion down, strategically between their drinks.

He looked first at Charlie letting a smile of frank appreciation cross his jowly face, and then turned his darting black orbs back towards Fear.

"Room in the bed for a little one?" he said with a leering grin.

DCI Davie Rothwell then laughed long and hard, and from behind his shoulder Jenkins sycophantically joined the chorus of mirth.

****

"What a lovely surprise!" said Rothwell pulling up a chair and licking his lips both to clean the foam of his pint from them and in singular appreciation of the confrontation that was about to come. Then he turned his gaze to Charlie: "In the words of the song 'Does Your Mamma Know'?"

From his side of the table Fear saw Charlie's sculpted jaw tighten slightly, but she took a sip from her Prosecco and kept her composure with icy aplomb: "My mother, Mr...?"

"Rothwell" he answered, scarcely bothering to stop a smirk spreading across his face.

"Is sadly no longer with us. But my father certainly does 'know', as you put it. Not that it's any of your business. But who, since you have decided to join us, are you?"

But before Rothwell could reply, Fear did so for him: "This is Detective Chief Inspector Rothwell and his ever-attentive lapdog Detective Sergeant Jenkins. Apparently they're joined at the hip!"

Jenkins, bristling in the background, couldn't help himself rising to the bait: "If we're joined at the hip, how come he's sitting down and I'm still standing."

"Jenkins, shh," Rothwell said softly, raising his hand.

"Excuse my Sergeant," he said with an ingratiating leer at Charlie. "We've no intention of spoiling your evening, my dear. But we couldn't pass up the chance to say hello to our friend, Mr Fear. To welcome him home. Because you've been away, haven't you?"

Fear met his gaze.

"A short business trip. Not that it's any business of yours."

"That rather depends on the business, doesn't it? And where were you conducting this business?"

A slight pause and, as there was no answer from Fear, he persevered: "Now come on, where you been, disappeared off the radar screen you did, but then I can see why you'd want to come back on it, yer bit o'fluff's a bit young for you ain't she, what's the gap, 20 years, at least? Christ, yer old enough to be her bleedin' faitha! You sure old one eye knows what yer up to and who you're up to it with…señorita?" At that Jenkins erupted into a laugh.

But Rothwell remained still and silent, necking his Schiehallion and keeping both Fear and Charlie under surveillance from his side of the table.

"Is that really any of your business, Jenkins? Now, if you don't mind we're in the middle of a private conversation, unless you have any official police business with me, I suggest you leave us alone," snapped Fear, the edge in his voice loud and clear.

Rothwell leaned across the table so that his heavy face and brooding black stare were only inches away from Fear's features: "But you know, Mr Fear, I think your business is exactly the type of business that is our duty to make our own. Why don't you answer my colleague's question...once again – where have you been for the past few days?"

Fear leaned back against the cushioned leather padding of the Chesterfield wall settee, folded his arms and sighed: "Since I thought your surveillance was of such top, round-the-clock quality, you ought to be able to tell me where I was and what I was doing there. In fact, if you were any good you'd be able to tell me where I've been before I even arrived there? But that's your problem, isn't it? You've been cut so much, you're really only part-timers, aren't you? Do your eight, nine, ten hours, or whatever it is, then you're home for your egg and chips and that's it for the day."

The reference to just the supper Jenkins had been looking forward to barely five minutes before goaded him into action. He took a step forward and leaned over Fear.

"You think you're so clever, don't you, Fear," he spat. "Just because you've been in the army and been trained to use an automatic. That doesn't impress me. Easy enough to shoot someone in the back. But that doesn't make you the big man, not in my book."

Fear noticed the young man's fist clenching and prepared himself for an assault.

But Rotherwell saw it too.

"Jenkins," he growled "Whatever you're thinking of doing, don't. We're in a public space surrounded by peace-loving citizens. So don't make an arse of yourself, son. Just drink up and lets bugger off home."

Looking like a schoolboy, Jenkins stepped back, glared daggers at Fear, and pushed his way roughly through the crowd, banging his unfinished pint on the bar.

"There," Rothwell said, "saved you bruising your knuckles knocking some sense into him. He's not a bad detective, actually. Just a bit feisty. Shoots from the hip, if you know what I mean. Trigger happy. All the things you were taught not to be in the SAS, Fear. Am I right, or am I right?"

Fear shrugged. Rothwell was likely to be far more trouble without the distraction of his yapping terrier of a sergeant.

Charlie looked from Fear to the Chief Inspector as though waiting for one of them to explain what was going on.

Fear took his cue from her look.

"Though we're delighted to see the back of DS Jenkins, I hope you don't think it impolite if I remind you that while infinitely preferable to four, three is still considered a crowd."

Rothwell's right hand slipped across the table and patted Charlie's slender fingers: "You know, young lady, that hanging about with people like your friend here only ever ends one way? Has Mr Fear told you anything about the disappearance of a local small-time drug dealer called Jimmy Bancroft, the massacre of a supposedly decommissioned IRA Active Service Unit, not to mention the complete wipe-out of a team of Aberdonian drug dealers. This last involving high calibre firearms, long-range shooting and a skill set in terms of surveillance and ambush that would only have been acquired by someone with specialist training such as Mr Fear had in the SAS?

Charlie's slender eyebrows raised and her eyes seemed to sadden, providing Rothwell with the answer he had been looking for.

"I thought not. But, young lady, what you have to do now is ask yourself just why your father, dear old Obadiah, has enlisted Mr Fear and what it is he does for his doubtless generous remuneration. Then you need to put two and two together and do your sums."

As Fear began to coil with the volcanic promise of more violence, Rothwell's right hand shot up placatingly, he quickly downed his pint, placed the empty glass on the table and stood up:

"If you do you will come to the only logical conclusion you can arrive at…which is that nothing either of them have been telling you adds up." Rothwell buttoned up his overcoat: "Good luck with that and good night, young lady," he said and then turned to Fear.

"The net is closing Fear, I promise you. Enjoy the rest of your evening."

And with that he headed to the door of the bar.

Charlie followed him with her eyes, then looked at Fear.

"What did Rothwell mean with all that talk of small-time drug dealers, the IRA and Aberdonian gangsters… were they all killed by you?"

Fear tried to quell the whirlpool of emotions that Rothwell had stirred up in him and let the anger dissipate.

Eventually he spoke: "Look, Charlie, when you've been where I've been, done what I've done and then ended up inside with your whole life played out in the media, well then there are going to be people who come back from your past to haunt you. Up on Sheriffmuir that's what came to pass, and it was either me or the IRA…just like it was 15 years back on the streets of the Bogside. Would you rather they had killed me?"

"No, I wouldn't and I can get my head around that. Just. But what about the small-time drug dealer and the Aberdonians. How do you explain their deaths?" she demanded, her eyes scorching him.

Fear frowned for a moment: "Yeah, Jimmy Bancroft was a minor drug dealer, but one who was dealing to high school kids and who couldn't help himself ripping your father off and trying to take some of his other business plays away from him. And for the record I didn't kill him. In fact, I tried to persuade him of the error of his ways. Unfortunately he didn't get the message and instead attempted to kill your dad. Luckily he failed. I guess you're happy with that?"

Charlie looked at him aghast. All this killing – and springing from her father's other 'business' interests. She was speechless, as a multitude of questions thronged to be asked.

Fear saw the answer to his question, 'How much did she know?' The answer was nothing. For a moment Fear was unsure whether he should go on…but having started, he saw no reason to stop: "Look, I'm sorry if what I'm telling you is news, but I don't see any point in keeping it from you… Maybe it's time for the whole truth, uncomfortable as it is."

He looked around to make sure no one was listening. This stuff was dynamite.

"Coming to our friends in the North East, they were a nasty bunch who were in league with the Russian Mafia. They were smuggling enough weaponry for a small war. If they hadn't been stopped when they were they would be on their way down the A90 armed to the teeth and bent on slaughter. Instead one night's work stopped a drugs war erupting that could well have seen innocents caught up in the crossfire."

Before he could complete his last sentence, Charlie stood up: "I'm sorry, but that's a hell of a lot to take in. I need time to…understand it," and with her eyes pooling with barely contained tears, she walked out of The Curly Coo.

Staring into his pint Ludovic Fear wondered if he would ever see Charlie MacPherson again.

39

THE DCI's office door was slightly ajar. DS Ricky Jenkins knocked and entered in one movement, smiling as he caught sight of his gaffer's size elevens parked on the desk.

The rest of Rothwell's ample body nestled comfortably in his desk chair, collar undone, blue silk tie hanging loose, shirt sleeves rolled up above the wrists but left pointing out, while his sharp dark eyes scanned the court pages of the *Stirling Observer* following the witty observations of his favourite reporter, Madonna Black.

After a momentary pause to take in a picture he had observed 100 times before, Jenkins broke the silence: "Could have something tasty for you the night, sir!"

Rothwell put down his paper and sipped from his cooling mug of coffee.

"Aye...that'll be a first then, Ricky, son!" he smiled.

"Anonymous call earlier the night tippin' us off about drugs being dumped at the auld Thompson farmhouse up on the Carse of Lecropt. The tout asked that the information be passed on to you in person, sir; apparently it might be linked to the disappearance of that shite Jimmy Bancroft," and with that Jenkins placed the information pro forma with the details on the desk in front of his gaffer.

"Anonymous informant? Another wild goose chase likely as not. D'ya think I've got the time or the inclination to go following up every bampot tip-off that comes my way?"

Rothwell picked up the Information report nonetheless and checked out the grading. It was a five, which suggested the information was highly credible.

"Worth a punt, surely? Come on, gaffer, it's a deed Tuesday night, the rain's pissin' down as per and there's little chance o' anything else happening the back o' one in the morning," Jenkins said, hoping his enthusiasm would prove infectious.

Rothwell smiled at the verbal game they had just played out. It had almost become a ritual. "Okay, maybees you have a point, Ricky, son, but before we go moochin' about derelict old farmhooses in the dark for this an' that, what's happening with the soldier boy and old one eye?"

The change in his gaffer's mood put Jenkins on the back foot, because the news on that front was anything but good: "No' great, boss. Fear has given our boys the slip, and no one seems to know where he is. But I'm afraid it gets even worse when it comes to MacPherson…" At which point he produced another slim dossier, from which he extracted a single photograph.

Rothwell picked it up casually but suddenly stared hard at it. "Bloody hell, it's The Cyclops and DCS Jimmy-friggin'-McColl – all cosy on the banks o' the Lake of Mentieth. Where did this come from, for Chrisssssakes?" said Rothwell, letting out a long slow whistle.

"Surveillance does pay off – despite what that murdering bastard Fear was saying in the Cosy Coo. Yup, our wee man with his big lens has done us proud. Aye bang to rights, boss, just like you say, as cosy as could be. At last, confirmation that they're as thick as thieves. So how do we play this? It's a big call."

Rothwell continued to study the still of MacPherson and McColl deep in conversation over their coffee cups before he eventually looked up at his number two: "This isn't going to be enough of itself to bring McColl down, but at least it confirms what we thought all along, that he is in The Cyclops' thrall. But we need to be careful we don't go over-playing our hand. "

"So what's our next move, boss?" Jenkins asked.

"Fucked if I know for the moment, Ricky, son," Rothwell said. "But following up tonight's tip-off might not be a bad move. We know Bancroft and The Cyclops were connected. A lead on Bancroft's killer could get us closer to nailing MacPherson." He looked up at the office clock. It was almost 2 am. "If we want to be catchin' us anything tonight we best get going. Tool up for this one, just in case. Let's get out to Lecropt pronto and make sure we're there waiting for them and not vice versa. It's gonna be a long night, and we'll have plenty of time to work out what's the best way to deal with that bent bastard McColl."

"Roger that," DS Jenkins said, trying to suppress his excitement.

****

The derelict farmhouse nestled not far from a fold of the River Forth.

A combination of ever-steepening prices and the grim financial grip of the supermarkets had eventually brought four generations of farming to an end. A developer had moved in to make an offer the family couldn't refuse.

Already one new estate had been thrown up, and there seemed to be no let-up in their plans to build more housing on every available square inch of land right up to the river edge, despite the inevitable flooding threat.

The broken roof and shattered stone walls of the old farmhouse were once again inhabited, albeit temporarily; for sitting on an upturned old bucket sat Detective Chief Superintendent Jimmy McColl.

Nervously he checked his Gold Cartier; it was 1 am, and the long hours had passed slowly, but all he could do was wait and hope that Rothwell and Jenkins had taken the bait and were on their way.

For the umpteenth time, he pulled out the standard issue Smith & Wesson M&P (Military and Police) 9mm and again checked the magazine with its 9 Parabellum rounds, before clicking it back into the handle of the gun, which he slotted into its shoulder holster.

He yawned, partly because he was tired and partly out of nervousness. But he knew he was ahead of the game in that he'd made it to the farmhouse first. If Rothwell and Jenkins did indeed let their curiosity get the better of them, the only road down onto the Carse would easily give him plenty of warning as the beam of any approaching vehicle's headlights would pierce the darkness. He'd have them in his sights before they had any idea of what awaited them in the shadows of the farmhouse.

McColl shook his head slightly as he admitted to himself this was the only option left to him. He'd known for a while that Rothwell had suspected his relationship with MacPherson was too close to be legitimate, and there'd been other slight hints that others had their doubts too.

And anyway, he had never taken to DCI Rothwell nor his aggressively pushy DS. Together they threatened everything he'd built up for himself and his family over the previous 30 years. Now they would pay the price. Once removed from the scene, his friendship with MacPherson would be restored and his gambling debts erased. Not a bad result for one night's dirty work. Indeed, if he had a debt of loyalty then it was the one that he owed MacPherson and extended all the way back to their childhood. It was far greater than anything he was due those two self-serving arrogant little shits of police officers, who would trample over anything that got in their way and that of their careers.

Because, with the demise of the old Central Scotland Police Force and the nine policing regions and the creation of the soulless behemoth that was Police Scotland, the reality was that life in the Police was now a case of every man for himself.

40

THE rain that had fallen steadily since they left Randolphfield and wound their way up through Bridge of Allan was getting noticeably heavier by the time the navy blue Ford Focus took the turn-off for the Carse of Lecropt.

Dominating the road down onto the Carse was the imposing Church of Lecropt, built between 1825 and 1827 to the designs of local architects David Hamilton and William Stirling on a long-established site of worship.

Its Gothic Revival profile proved a useful landmark, signalling the left turn from the A9 down to the southern part of the Carse and its rich alluvial farmland.

As the Focus began to wind its way down the hill the rain seemed to increase in intensity, almost drowning the headlights with a blizzard of droplets and drumming the roof so loudly that the two detectives could hardly hear themselves think.

"With the rain pissin' down like this I'll bet we're onto plums boss. Who in their right minds are gonna be out fuckin' around in an auld derelict farmhouse?" Jenkins moaned.

Rothwell continued to stare relentlessly into the night: "But that's the exact reason why there is likely to be something going on. Any felon with half a brain is in turn going to be saying to himself that no copper in his right mind is going to be out and about in this downpour searching old farmhouses in the middle of nowhere on a night like this. Naah, Ricky, son, I'd say it is the perfect night for any self-respecting drug smuggler to be up to his tricks."

Jenkins' two hands clutched the vehicle steering wheel at ten-to-two, and his eyes continued to peer through the windscreen as he concentrated on a road that was almost single-lane and also starting to deteriorate worryingly in quality. The Focus' front right tyre dropped into a hidden pothole that shook the vehicle and its two occupants to their core. He let out a startled shriek: "Bastard!" shouted the DS. "How far is it? At this rate we'll be lucky to get there with four wheels on the wagon."

"Aren't you supposed to be the one that has all the answers, Detective Sergeant? "Another quarter of a mile, I reckon. As my old driving instructor used to say: 'If you can't see, slow down.' Good advice. We'll get there soon enough, according to the CI [Crime Informant] sheet it has a broken gate hanging to the right-hand side of the turn off."

Sure enough after another few minutes of rally driving the lane leading to the Thompson farm was picked up in the beam of their headlights, and Jenkins turned the Focus onto a track that was even worse than the one that had threatened to explode their tyres for the last mile.

As the DS threaded the Focus along through even more potholes, wincing at every lurch and creak that shuddered through the vehicle, the ramshackle whitewashed walls of the old farm buildings were lit up in the full beam of the headlights, and then there in front of them was the old house itself, half its roof blown off by last winter's storms and its windows roughly boarded up.

"Kinda sad, to think that was once a home," Rothwell mused.

"Looks more like a set for a horror movie," Jenkins said as he pulled up the handbrake.

Okay, it's naw lookin' too good, but that don't mean we switch off and end up in walking into something tasty."

Spreading an aerial photo of the farmhouse and its surrounding acres on his knees, Rothwell clicked on the interior light and said: "First we'll make a sweep of the house and then hit the outbuildings. There's a barn at the back, which might be interesting, but just make sure you get the Maglite on and keep the beam nice and steady."

"No bother, boss," Jenkins said, eyeing the layout.

"Remember anyone already here will have seen our headlights for the last twenty minutes, and this old bus isn't exactly discreet. So if there's anyone around, they're not going to be taken by surprise. Let's stay focused."

"Copy that, boss," Jenkins said, as both men got out of the car.

They jogged across the short distance between the vehicle and the farmhouse, desperately trying to avoid a soaking, which proved impossible. Jenkins' Maglite lit their way, and as they walked in through the doorway its beam swept the room from side-to-side for signs of life.

There were none.

The farmhouse roof, no more than a mixture of broken spars, provided only pitiful cover from the lashing rain. But as Jenkins' foot creaked on a piece of debris a rustle in the shadows was followed by the jostle of feathers and three pigeons, captured on Jenkins' trembling, arcing beam, flew through the roof.

"For fuck's sake," Jenkins said under his breath.

"Jeeeez, will you hold that thing steady," snapped Rothwell.

"Sorry," Jenkins said, sweeping the beam around them. Still, now they were here, there was a job to be done. Staying extremely close to each other, they worked their way steadily through all the rooms in the derelict farmhouse.

As each and every area of darkness and shadow was illuminated it proved empty, other than the scuttling shapes of the rats that had clearly taken up residence in the old farmhouse.

As one giant slick rodent scurried over Rothwell's right foot it was the DCI's turn to startle: "For fuck's sake, did you see that? It was the size of a bleedin' Jack Russell!"

Jenkins politely but firmly prised the gaffer's hand off his arm. He'd have a bruise there in the morning.

"Come on, boss. Stay calm."

"And carry on. Well, you try and stay calm when you've got a rat trying to run up your trouser leg."

Finally they reached the last bedroom. Plaster sagged from the ceiling, and through the slipped tiles above you could see into the dark density of the night. Downstairs again, they took a last look round.

"Looks like somebody has yanked our chain," Rothwell said. "But I guess we might as well check the outbuildings before we go."

Jenkins, shivering and soaked, shrugged his shoulders in a gesture of unconvincing acquiescence and reluctantly led the way through the back door. The Maglite illuminated the rotten double doors of a barn across the yard.

Rothwell followed the beam of his Maglite towards two fractured wooden doors that almost covered the entrance of the barn towards the rear of the farmyard.

Hesitating at the front of the doors as one of them swung back and banged against the barn, blown by the stinging wind, he couldn't help himself: "Ten to one I'll bet the barn is overrun with more of those monster rats. I'd wager good money on it being like a scene from a bleedin' James Herbert book."

"Just open the doors and sweep the place with the light and then we can call it a day, get back to HQ and get the kettle on for a cuppa." the DCI said.

Jenkins did as he was told, pulling the left-hand door open and pushing past it into the dark of the barn with Rothwell right behind him.

He hadn't walked more than a couple of yards before he stood on something that gave a loud screech: "Christ almighty! I bleedin' knew it…" almost before the words had escaped his mouth the two detectives found themselves illuminated in a brilliant glare far more powerful than Jenkins' Maglite.

"What's wrong, gentlemen? Weren't you expecting company?" There was a laugh from behind what must, Rothwell thought, be an arc light. A familiar laugh.

Shielding his eyes, Rothwell shouted: "What the fuck… is that you, McColl?"

****

"That's no way to address your superior officer, DCI Rothwell, especially as he's been waiting so patiently for you. Turn your lamp off, DS Jenkins. Mine outranks it, just as I outrank you."

Jenkins hesitated for a moment, but Rothwell whispered: "Do what he says."

Stepping into the light, the sight of the 9mm in McColl's right hand pointing their way provided the DS with all the persuasion he needed to comply.

"Smart boy, Jenkins," McColl said, "but then that has always been your problem, hasn't it, Detective Sergeant - you've always been a bit too smart for your own good and now look where it has got you…"

But before McColl could finish, Rothwell, his voice filled with rage, snapped: "And where exactly would that be, McColl? On the tail of a rotten copper who has been on the payroll of Central Scotland's biggest crim for years? We know what you've been up to, and we've got the evidence. Enjoy your little tête-à-tête at the Lake of Mentieth Hotel the other day?"

"A legitimate meeting with a valued and registered informant. And no long-distance photo can prove otherwise. I've had a professional relationship with Obadiah MacPherson that stretches back before the ink was even dry on your warrant card, Rothwell. It's a relationship that has saved Central Scotland Police and the Stirling area from a string of heinous crimes that would have put our public in grave danger, had it not been for the information I received from MacPherson."

But Rothwell, despite the fact he was literally staring down the barrel of a gun, would not be denied: "Central Scotland Police ceased to exist six months ago. But then that's all part of your problem McColl, isn't it? You can't accept change, can't accept the fact you are no longer the big fish in a small pond. Obadiah is it? I had always wondered what MacPherson's first name was. No wonder he doesn't want it made public knowledge. Any more than you want your dealings with him exposed to the glare of publicity. All very commendable, McColl, but how much was The Cyclops really into you for? And don't come the innocent. The word on the street is that you owe his Bookies at least 100 large."

The slight tremble in the S&W underlined the level of rage that was now surging through McColl, and he flicked the handgun towards the sodden ground: "You would do well to remember, DCI Rothwell, that it's me who is holding the gun! Now both of you unholster your side arms and place them end of the barrel first on the deck," and as they started to do so McColl added: "Easy, easy," before the two handguns clattered to the ground hitting the mixture of dirt and broken floorboards.

"So what now?" Jenkins demanded defiantly.

McColl barked out a harsh laugh: "Why, the tragic and untimely demise of two hero detectives, cut down in their prime in the line of duty, while trying to apprehend unknown felons, and whose bravery will be remembered and revered by their grieving colleagues for as long as there is a police force in Scotland. Presumably even you can work out the end of this particular crime, DS Jenkins?"

"You think you'll get away with it, McColl? Is it worth it – murder two fellow officers, just to cover your slippery tracks?" Rothwell challenged.

"What I'm going to do is stop two grasping, treacherous wannabees ruining a relations hip that has served this force tremendously well, in order to promote their own unbridled, vaulted ambition. But the time for talking is done. Get on your knees – both of you – with your hands on your heads."

"You've gotta be jokin'" Jenkins blustered desperately, his voice trembling with anger and fear in equal measure "… surely you ain't goin' through with this?"

"I'm afraid you've left me no option. But what I will do is give you a choice…who wants to meet his maker first? Because the other will be left to bury him."

"You've lost the bleedin' plot, McColl, you're never gonna get away with this…no way," spat Rothwell.

"Oh I think I will be just fine, my brave boys. After all, you were lured to your death by an anonymous tip-off…what the hell has that got to do with me? But your reticence is disconcerting, so what I will do is help you regain your decision-making powers." McColl then fished into his anorak pocket and produced a pound coin: "So what's it going to be, Rothwell, heads or tails? I think the senior officer's prerogative should apply, don't you, DS Jenkins?"

Rothwell and Jenkins eyed each other in despair, terror writ large across their features, but neither was prepared to make the call.

"You disappoint me, gentlemen; but that is nothing new, so we will go with heads for you, DCI Rothwell, and tails for your boy," said McColl sarcastically, drawing out the last word; and then with his left thumb he flicked the coin into the air.

It sparkled in the brilliant light, and for a moment McColl's enthralled gaze followed it as though it were a diamond.

But his concentration had wandered momentarily and Rothwell, whose gaze had never wavered, saw this and used the opportunity to scrabble a handful of dust and grit from the floor by his side. The coin fell, and McColl stooped to see whose side had come up.

"It's heads, so, DCI Rothwell, it seems you must lead by example."

But before McColl could continue, Rothwell launched his handful of sweepings, following them with his own body like a human projectile.

Yet McColl managed to get a shot off, and the barn rang with the report and the ricochet of the bullet off the wall. But there was no chance of a second shot as Rothwell wrapped himself around his would-be executioner in a ferocious bearhug.

Jenkins followed his boss, throwing himself into the melee and launching a haymaker over Rothwell's shoulder.

"Never mind hitting him – get the fucking gun off him," the DCI shouted, and Jenkins rolled over and ripped the weapon from McColl's grasp.

Rothwell relaxed and started pulling his senior officer to his feet.

"Now you can hit him," he said, punching McColl in the stomach. He bent double with pain, gasping for breath.

"The game's over," Rothwell barked, grabbing McColl by the collar and forcing his head up.

"Right, you piece of shit, tell us what MacPherson is up to. We know something's afoot. Telling us what it is might just shave a year or two off what is going to be a very long sentence, McColl."

"Go to hell," McColl managed to gasp.

Rothwell's upper cut knocked him over backwards. The only cry came from the DCI, who shook his aching hand. McColl lay motionless on the floor.

"Steady on, boss. You can't just beat him up."

"Just fuckin watch me," Rothwell said. "Resisting arrest. Two of us to one of him. Who do you think they're going to believe?" He raised a foot and slammed it down on one of McColl's knees.

The Chief Superintendent came back to consciousness with a muted scream and started squirming away from his tormentor. Rothwell stamped on the other knee. This time the scream was piercing. Rothwell laughed at the pathetic attempt to slither out of range and raised his foot once more.

But before he could inflict more damage, McColl's body underwent a convulsion, and his feet kicked Rothwell hard on the ankles, making him fall over awkwardly. At the same time McColl's right arm reached backwards for one of the guns he'd kicked behind him and now swung it up with deadly intent. Jenkins, still holding McColl's original weapon, had a split second to make his decision.

Two shots rang out simultaneously, and Rothwell slumped heavily on the floor.

"Oh God, are you a'right, boss?" Jenkins shouted, staring down at the two motionless bodies.

Eventually the broad back of the DCI began to move. Rothwell rolled over, shading his eyes from the arc light.

"Fuck's sake, man," he mumbled, "You nearly fuckin' shot me." He sat up and looked down at McColl, from whose chest a steady stream of blood was seeping.

"Christ, did I kill him?" Jenkins looked aghast.

"You did, son. A very commendable bit of quick thinking. You saved my life, and I thank you for it. Now give me a hand up, and we'll have a wee think about what's best to do now."

The first thing the DCI decided to do was retrieve the half bottle of whisky he'd secreted in the glove compartment of the Focus.

"You, too, son. That's an order – it's good for the shock."

Jenkins took a swig and immediately started coughing.

Rothwell shook his head and laughed. "You'll learn, son, you'll learn." He took another swig and wiped his mouth with the back of his hand, pausing to wiggle his fingers. "That's going to hurt in the morning. And you're right, Jenkins, the old bastard's going to look like he was in a fight before he met his timely demise. So what's to do? You know the truth, and I know the truth; but can we prove it? As McColl said himself, a photo doesn't prove anything definitively. We don't know who else MacPherson may have in his pocket, but if he's still got influence we might find ourselves being stitched up. We can't trust anyone in the force anymore. So…" he drank again: "this is what I think, Jenkins. Why don't you get that jerry can of petrol out the boot, and then we'll move the DCS to a more flammable environment and give him a funeral pyre the fuckin' Vikings would have been proud of. What d'you think?"

"But what's our story, boss?"

"Leave that to me, sonny. I'll have something worked out before the first fire engine arrives, trust me. Now, let's get moving."

Jenkins smiled crookedly and did as he was bid, and within moments the two of them were being warmed by

McColl's burning corpse. Staring into the flames Rothwell said: "We've got a shit-storm coming our way, Ricky, son, but before it erupts we need to make sure we are fireproof!" and then his frazzled laughter burst out above the fat spattered flames crackling just yards away.

41

CHARLIE MacPherson guided her Mini along Kenilworth Road between the mansions that gave the street its reputation as the most moneyed in Stirling but took in none of the architectural grandeur, such was the intensity of her dilemma – her head was still thronged with the revelations DCI Rothwell's questions had provoked.

How should she react to the unpalatable truth of her father's unofficial business – and to Fear's confession of what he did to protect that business. How could she love a self-confessed killer?

She hoped that an hour or so in the gym would at least calm the turmoil inside her.

Situated at the very top of the old Victorian Spa town lay the Bridge of Allan Sports club, whose gym, built on an old squash court, boasted all the equipment necessary for the intensity of workout she needed to exorcise her angst, however temporarily.

It was always so peaceful up here, and many times she had promised herself that she would go for a walk along one of the many paths that threaded the nearby Minewood and find the old 16th-century copper mine which supplied the mint at Stirling Castle in medieval times.

But with what was left of the evening's light starting to fade, her long promised hike would have to wait for another day again. Now as Charlie changed down the Mini's gears and turned into Mine Road all she sought was the balm of the endorphins she hoped to release during her impending workout.

She turned into the club car park and reached for the kit bag on the passenger seat. But as she did so, she saw that a navy blue Ford Focus had drawn to a halt in the bay next to her.

Both of the vehicle's doors shot open, and to her astonishment the two cops who had helped shatter her dreams just days before jumped out of either side.

Rothwell's bald dome materialised at her driver's window, and the DCI quickly pulled out his warrant card, placed it against the glass pane, smiled sweetly and signalled to Charlie to let the window down.

As it slid low Rothwell nodded his head curtly: "Charlotte MacPherson, I am detaining you under section 14 of the Criminal Procedure (Scotland) Act 1995, because I suspect you of having committed an offence punishable by imprisonment, namely of being an accessory to the murder of Detective Chief Superintendent James McColl. Of withholding vital information in relation to that crime in relation to your father Obadiah MacPherson and one Ludovic Fear."

At the other side of the vehicle Jenkins couldn't wait to play his part in the unfolding drama: "Charlotte MacPherson, you will now be detained to enable further investigation to be carried out regarding the offence and as to whether or not you should be arrested. You will now be taken to a place of detention and will be informed of your rights in respect of said detention."

Before she could even mouth a reply, Rothwell reached in and took her ignition key, slipping it into his pocket. Then he opened the door for her.

Climbing out of the Mini, Charlie recovered from her shock and began to protest her innocence: "Are you out of your tiny minds…I don't have a clue what you're on about… I've never heard of a Detective Chief Superintendent James McColl. I demand…"

"All in good time, Miss," Rothwell said, putting a restraining hand on her shoulder.

Charlie shrugged it off, her eyes blazing.

"You are so going to regret this."

Rothwell ignored her and indicated that DS Jenkins should see her to the unmarked police car, while he closed the Mini's window and locked it.

But this time it was Rothwell who was to be surprised. Before the DCI could answer her, the air was filled with a verbal volley from the court immediately adjacent to the car park.

"Do you mind, we're trying to finish a game of tennis here. This is a private club. Anyway, that's no way to be treating a young lady," snapped a dark-haired man, his eyes burning with the intensity of sporting battle, who bore an amazing resemblance to the Spanish tennis ace David Ferrer.

On the other side of the net his shiny headed opponent, who Charlie had met in the gym a couple of times and had always thought looked Mexican, quickly asked: "Everything all right, Miss?"

But before she could reply Rothwell was brandishing his warrant card in their direction: "This is official police business, and I couldn't give a flying fuck if you were Andy Murray and Roger-bleedin'-Federer, no one gets in the way of the law. Now if you don't want to find yourselves banged up for a Breach of the Peace, private tennis club or not, I suggest you finish your game and mind your own business."

While his superior officer was barking out this dire threat, Jenkins had already started to guide Charlie into the back of the Focus, and within moments Rothwell had jumped into the vehicle driver's seat and reversed the CID vehicle, leaving the two tennis players glowering in their slipstream.

Once they were all in the Ford Focus, Rothwell glanced in the mirror, enjoying the glimpse of Charlie's immaculate blonde hair, long lashes and the honeyed brown of her eyes. Throw in her undoubtedly fit body and that intoxicating voice and he could see why Fear had fallen for her. Who wouldn't?

They wove down Well Road, turned left along Henderson Street and passed the peeling splendour of The Royal Hotel. Rothwell couldn't help himself making a dig: "Aye, it's about time someone bought The Royal and got the old girl back on her feet. A perfect job for that well-known local hotelier and entrepreneur Obadiah MacPherson, don't you think, Miss MacPherson – or is your father too busy with something much more interesting?"

Charlie's chocolate gaze locked on Rothwell's as she replied icily: "I haven't the faintest idea what you're talking about, detective..."

Rothwell smiled benignly: "Oh I think you do. But while we are enjoying each other's company can I ask you a question...has anyone ever told you that you bear a striking resemblance to Dusty Springfield?"

Charlie's eyes met the DCI's but she said nothing.

To her right Jenkins interjected: "Oh come on, Miss MacPherson – or can I call you Charlie? You're among friends now, and it's time you appreciated just how much shit you are in. Central Scotland's highest ranking detective has been brutally murdered just after he was pictured in a rather intense meeting with yer old man, who, along with his henchman – your boyfriend – has disappeared off the face of the earth, you can't really think we are so naïve that we would think you don't have a Scooby about all of that?"

Charlie inclined her head in Jenkins' direction, and the scorn that was written across her refined features stung him like the back of a hand: "I really don't care what someone like you thinks; now if you don't mind I would like to call my lawyer the minute we arrive at Randolphfield."

With that she turned her head sharply and stared out at the passing street scene.

"Of course," Rothwell said, "when you get to Randolphfield."

But as the vehicle took a right turn into Upper Bridge Street, the realisation hit Charlie that Police Headquarters was not their destination.

Continuing his surveillance of her in the rear view mirror, Rothwell enjoyed the shock of that realisation as it swept over Charlie's face, but she said nothing.

Her attention was soon snapped from the DCI's assessing gaze when Jenkins grabbed her wrists and proceeded to wrap them in black plastic binding.

As they turned down into Irvine Place, slowing to a halt just outside what had once been an imposing four-storey town house, now converted into flats, Rothwell turned round and rested his left hand on the back of the front passenger seat.

His smile was sickly sweet: "For your information, Miss MacPherson, I am under no obligation from the Criminal Procedure Act to detain you in a Police Station, so you will begin your detention in another suitable place while we see if your time with us helps loosen your tongue."

Then his dark eyes flicked towards Jenkins: "Get her mobile."

Jenkins barked a short harsh laugh: "With pleasure! Now which pocket is it in, darlin'? You don't want my hands to be rummaging where they should'ne be, sweetheart, eh?"

Charlie's eyes dipped towards her hoody's pouch pocket and Jenkins slipped his right hand in, as her shoulders snapped back and her body went rigid.

As he leaned across her, Jenkins turned his head slightly so that his mouth was less than an inch from hers, then he whispered: "Nice and cosy back here isn't it, sweetheart?"

From the front Rothwell's voice brought his subordinate back to heel: "Cut that out, Ricky, will you?" but as his hand located and retrieved the mobile Jenkins let his nose, ever so slightly, brush Charlie's cheek and he whispered: "Till later…sweetheart."

Then he pulled clear and handed the mobile to Rothwell, who had parked the car outside a nondescript block of flats.

"So what cute little pet name have you given your soldier boy?" asked the DCI as he scrolled down the list of entries in the names section, but before Charlie could answer he let out a satisfied gasp: "Aaah, but of course, Ludo!" Then Rothwell started to tap out a text.

Charlie couldn't stop her concern breaking into words: "What're you doing?"

Rothwell smiled serenely: "Why I'm sending lover boy a little request to come and meet his girl…the only problem is that you, my dear Miss MacPherson, will be tucked up all nice and warm with DS Jenkins babysitting you in our safe house in the top flat here, while I wait for your boyfriend to come calling somewhere more appropriate. You see we must make sure Ludo doesn't do anything rash…that we might all regret."

The two detectives began to laugh. It was not a pleasant sound.

42

FEAR sat glued to a History Channel special on the Hunt for Hitler, which had been made using newly public FBI files from 1947 to put together an incredible hypothesis that the Nazi tyrant had escaped to South America from his Berlin bunker, when the text announced its arrival on his mobile via the usual 'ketchoo' of a bottle top being levered off.

Seeing her name flash up he almost dropped the handset, such was his haste to read the text: 'We need to talk! Can we meet up on the castle esplanade in 30 mins? Charlie xxx'.

Fear, replied 'Sure' far too quickly and was already grabbing his Barbour jacket from the hall coat peg and opening the front door, when he actually started to digest the content of the text and what it could mean.

As always the voice in his head was keen to help: 'We need to talk? It's 50/50 mate, you're either buggered or it's a case of hope springs eternal.'

Fear went with hope, and before he knew it he was swinging the Volumex onto the cobblestones that led the final 100 yards up to Stirling Castle's Esplanade and its mighty sweeping panoramic views.

Majestic in the dying embers of the day, the citadel sat atop the crag of Castle Hill. Fear took in the situation with a soldier's eye. They couldn't have chosen a better site for it.

Until the 1890s the castle had strategically dominated the farthest downstream crossing of the River Forth while most of its present buildings had been constructed between 1490 and 1600 when Stirling had been developed as a principal royal centre by the Stewart kings, James III, James IV and James V.

But Fear's historical review was interrupted by the sight of a familiar car making its way to the car park. He narrowed his eyes as he saw DCI Rothwell climbing out of the Ford Focus. What the hell?

Seeing him, the bulky detective gave a finger-wiggling wave. Fear didn't like this at all. Where was Charlie, for starters? And what was that fat toad of a copper with a mocking smile doing there? It couldn't be a coincidence,

He jumped out of the Volumex, all the time his eyes never leaving the DCI, who had now turned around to enjoy the view out over the former royal medieval gardens of the King's Knot.

Fear strode over to join him. "Where is she, Rothwell?" he demanded without any preliminaries.

The DI kept his eyes on the fading green verde below him: "I'm assuming you mean your girlfriend? Under a watchful eye, tucked up safe and sound, where she will remain until you give me exactly what I want."

The sting of a vicious winter gale couldn't hit Fear as hard as the realisation that he had been played and that Charlie's life was the bait in the trap that Rothwell had set for him.

"Which is?" he snapped.

Rothwell turned to face him: "You know this could have been so much easier…nobody need have been hurt, if you'd just listened to me way back when. What I want is what I've always wanted: Obadiah MacPherson on a plate and before he pulls off whatever it is he has up his sleeve," answered the DCI amicably enough.

Fear felt for the 9-milly in his pocket, and moving close to Rothwell he stuck the barrel into his ample flank.

Then his patience snapped, and he grabbed Rothwell by the anorak and span him round until he was holding him over the wall, his sweating, florid features now hanging above the ancient parapet: "Do you know what this is, Rothwell?"

"I'm guessing you're not that pleased to see me, so yes, I know what it is. And I also know – or think I know – you're not stupid enough to shoot a police officer in a public place. So can the histrionics and let's talk like adults."

Fear looked about him. There were still a few sightseers strolling around, a couple of cars pulled into the car park. He relaxed his hold on Rothwell, but he was still seething.

"I couldn't give a fuck what you want, but I'll promise you this: as God is my witness, Rothwell, if anything happens to Charlie you're a dead man. Now where is she?" Fear demanded.

Despite his breathless predicament and the terror that shone from his dark eyes, Rothwell gritted his teeth: "We both know I can't tell you that until you deliver for me. But I give you my word that if you turn Queen's evidence for us against The Cyclops, then you and Miss MacPherson will both walk away from this as free as birds."

Fear gave the man a stony glare: "And tell me, Rothwell, just how turning her old man into a lifer and bringing down his whole organisation is going to set me free to walk off into the sunset with MacPherson's only daughter? What do you take me for…a performing-fuckin'-monkey?"

His rage increasing by the moment, Fear shook the DCI viciously, and as his upper body hung over the side, 200 feet above the ground, a vein in Rothwell's neck started to bulge and spasm.

His breath rasping, Rothwell's belief that he had the ex-soldier between a rock and a hard place appeared to be lessening by the second: "For Christ sakes, Fear, you're in it up to your neck. We'll get you for at least one of those murders, if not all of them. What I'm offering you is a choice between your life back and life back behind bars. What happens after that is nothing to do with me. One way or another I will bring The Cyclops down and if you don't help me you will be going with him; and this time when you go inside they'll throw away the fuckin' key, you maniac."

Fear yanked the DCI back from the precipice but held him tight against the ancient stone wall: "For starters, you'll never see Charlie MacPherson alive again, and I promise you her father will hold you accountable for her death. Grow up: you can't go throwing your weight around like a cartoon character and expect to get away with it forever. You're fucked, Fear. I have you by the baws, pure and simple, now face the facts and get on with it," spat Rothwell through gritted teeth.

Fear's fist clenched, and the urge to plunge it into the middle of Rothwell's fat, sweaty face was almost irresistible. But he knew that would play into the detective's hands. He was deliberately trying to provoke him.

Sensing the outcome of Fear's internal struggle, Rothwell gave him a knowing smile. But almost before his lips had twitched, Fear spun him round and smashed a right hand of his jaw.

The DCI was launched through the air and landed with a thud on the turf. For a moment he remained stationary, but after a few seconds Rothwell propped himself up on unsteady elbows and dabbed at the blood spilling from his mouth. Gradually a vicious smile splintered his face: "You have 24 hours, soldier boy. If I don't have a call or a text to your girlfriend's mobile by then you're fucked...and so is she. You'll only have yourself to blame for it. How could you live with that on your conscience Fear? Have I made that simple enough for you?"

43

As the Volumex sped along the A84, Fear tried doggedly to blot out the desperate straits he now found himself in; but even the rush of adrenaline that a combination of the throaty roar of the engine and the vicious surges of acceleration brought him failed to provide any balm.

'He's right, you're fucked mate, pure and simple. Turn Queen's evidence and Charlie lives but will never be yours; don't and Christ knows what Rothwell and Jenkins have planned for her...plus you're never gonna be free of the bastards,' chimed the voice in his head helpfully.

Shaking said head ruefully, Fear realised that if he didn't play ball with his tormentors then his hopes of ever seeing Monty and building a proper relationship with his son, whatever Gina had in mind, would be dead in the water. Fear knew he only had one choice.

But first he had to find Lanarkyngs Castle, a deserted, derelict edifice that The Cyclops had chosen as the location for their rendezvous; probably for its remote fastness, perched on the south bank of the River Teith between Doune and Callendar.

Fear's mind kept returning to the events of the weeks that had spanned his release from incarceration and marked his involvement with The Cyclops.

Replaying the firefight with Doyle, the voice in his head repeated those last spite-riven words to the Provo's son, Johnny: 'You've moved on at last, focker.' Their bitter irony seeped through his very being. He knew that what he had become, what all these hours of training within The Regiment he would always love had made him, just wouldn't allow him to do so.

Yet his work for The Cyclops was indeed proving to be lucrative, as the 50K that had been deposited in his bank account for the Spanish job had proven, and now he was heading into a meeting which was going to spell out exactly what his role in 'the project', as MacPherson liked to call it, was all about.

Fear had no doubt that the risks involved in a job of the apparent magnitude of the one that The Cyclops had planned would make his escape to the life he wanted all but impossible. So what if they pulled it off? The fallout would be such that he'd be no more than a fugitive.

And now there was the situation with Charlie.

As for Monty, how could he even arrange visiting rights, never mind contest custody, with the turbulence he was about to enter looming large?

At least he'd made contact with his lawyers and instructed them to put the wheels in motion; but where would that really lead? The gut-wrenching thought that his son would be better off by far with Gina and 'Ross from the PTA' made him feel nauseous. He assumed this was because it was the simple truth, and he couldn't deal with it.

Gripping the leather-sheathed steering wheel, Fear's jaw set hard, and he tried to drive the doubts and self-loathing from his being.

Soon the forests to his left started to be punctuated by majestic half-hidden crenelated towers and Bartisans, which evoked an almost mystical Gothic landscape that took his breath away and provided the distraction he craved.

This, then, was his first sighting of the crumbling grandeur of Lanarkyngs Castle.

He tenderly eased down through the gears and manoeuvred into the mouth of a driveway that had clearly once led to something very substantial.

The gatehouse lodge that flanked it survived but in ruins. The two wrought-iron gates rested rusted and broken but hung partially open. As Fear looked up the driveway he saw that the vegetation and forestry that had clearly claimed the entrance had been recently cleared back to allow a vehicle to enter the estate.

Increasingly he realised that the meeting he was about to attend was likely to define his life and the fact that MacPherson had gone to the trouble of locating it in this ancient and ruined pile on the banks of the Teith began to fill him with dread.

Fear saw that he now had to drive across a rusted iron bridge, its paintwork long since bleached, the white rusted spars that were left an aching indictment of those that had allowed the estate to fall into such tragic ruin.

Yet the view of the Teith that gushed below made Fear crawl across the bridge as he savoured the magnificent sweep 100 feet below him. It was breath-taking, and he wondered what it must have been like to drive a carriage or ride a horse over this neglected iron span that was still, somehow, a monument to an age of splendour, almost forgotten and hidden in this Stirlingshire forest.

In the distance stood a towering but gnarled chestnut tree and beyond it lay the faded majesty of Lanarkyngs, a shell of its former imposing Gothic glory, yet still dominating the vista ahead.

It was then that the thought hit Fear that, for whatever reason The Cyclops had brought him to this shattered ruin, denouement was rapidly approaching...and from more than one angle.

He parked to the right of the castle's turreted entrance and wondered at the architecture. Although the roof had clearly almost completely collapsed, smoke still billowed from a partially erect chimney tower 50 feet to the left of the once imposing entrance.

But he did not have time to marvel: the green Jaguar parked only yards away made it clear The Cyclops was home.

Fear made his way on foot over moss and back onto gravel. There in between the front entrance turrets stood MacPherson: "Welcome to Lanarkyngs, Mr Fear. Why don't you come in?" he said, smiling grimly.

They picked their way through the broken timbers and fractured walling that lay in the hall, and Fear's gaze was caught by a triple arch that, flanked by once imposing mahogany-panelled walls, provided a view of what would have, in years gone by, been an intricate stairway, turning at right angles back on itself and leading upstairs to now God-knows-what.

Inwardly Fear ached for this once magnificent building that had been left to rot, but as he did so the voice in his head kept asking: 'So why has MacPherson brought you here of all places?'

The Cyclops turned left into a corridor that was full of pigeon droppings, broken tiles and pools of brackish brown water: "It's enough to make your heart bleed," said MacPherson with feeling.

"Aye, it is that. It must have been some place in its day. The view from the old iron bridge alone is bloody breathtaking! But I'm assuming you've some use for it, and we aren't here just for cultural purposes?"

As they reached the end of the corridor MacPherson turned left into a small room, which Fear supposed must once have been a servants' communal room. The delicious peat-reek of a fire burning brightly from a chipped marble and plaster fireplace that had somehow remained in working order permeated the air with its wondrous earthy scent and left Fear feeling like he had uncorked a bottle of Lagavulin.

To the left of the fireplace was a scuffed multi-drawered mahogany writing desk and a torn leather-backed chair, which MacPherson sat down on. As he did, Fear heard the arrival of a third party behind him.

Turning slowly, he was not surprised to see the hulking presence of Vallance in the splintered doorway: "Awright, Fear? You took yer time…eh?"

He smiled amicably: "Lanarkyngs isn't the easiest place to find, in case you haven't noticed, Vallance. Especially with the gatehouse derelict and almost completely overgrown with vegetation. Still, you've done well to make the driveway usable and the view from the iron bridge is…" Fear opened his hands in front of him to underline his appreciation.

"Aye, yer naw jokin'. You'll get some o' the best fishin' on the Teith from the beat below. Whit do you make o' the hoose?"

It was the longest passage of speech that didn't have to do with work Fear had ever heard from MacPherson's henchman, and it took him by surprise: "Something else in its day, no doubt about it. Odd name though?" he said, turning a quizzical look on MacPherson.

"The name Lanarkyngs is taken from the Old Brittonic word Llanerch which means a clearing in a forest," replied MacPherson from the desk, which had an ancient square-bottomed black telephone that must have dated back to the 1930s resting on top of it.

"In case you're wondering, Mr Fear, Old Brittonic was the language of the Celtic people known as the Britons which, by the sixth century, had split into various Brittonic languages like Welsh, Cumbric, Cornish and Breton. But enough of the history lesson. Clearly you'll be wondering why I've asked you to come here?"

"Clearly," echoed Fear.

MacPherson reclined back against the chair and stretched his legs out, then reached up and yanked on the shredded remnants of an old velvet pull chord, and somewhere down the corridor Fear heard a bell ring.

"Before our company arrives it's time you appreciated the importance of Lanarkyngs to me, Mr Fear. For that is not the only name the old place is known by, and indeed I prefer it by its other less romantic title...Castle MacPherson!"

Fear's eyes opened large in surprise at The Cyclops' revelation, yet he said nothing.

By contrast, MacPherson plainly couldn't wait to continue: "Obviously it's no coincidence that my name is MacPherson and we are here in Castle MacPherson...you see, I am in fact the bastard of Castle MacPherson and this once splendorous residence is all mine."

But before Fear could formulate a coherent reply a new presence loomed.

Johnny The Shark had arrived.

44

"El Agente Grant, buenos días, amigo!" said Johnny, a huge smile breaking across his face: "You surprised to see me again, matey?"

Fear shook his head: "You could say that. Certainly I thought you must have some use for our mutual friend here, since he went to all the trouble of having your mates terminated and then had me wrap you up in cotton wool for air mail back home to Blighty!"

"Cotton wool? You butcher my mates, dangle me over a soddin' balcony a couple o'hundred feet up, threaten to blow me bleedin' brains out 'cos I don't believe you're called Fear and then kidnap me, and you wonder why I tried to do a runner? You bleedin' jocks ain't half got a weird sense of humour, matey!" laughed Johnny.

Across the room MacPherson smiled wanly, his one eye angularly sweeping the three other figures in the room: "Okay, Fear, now you have been reacquainted with your old chum, listen closely as you might find the following…interesting. Johnny has been acting as, you might call it, a sleeper within The Foremen organisation and one that's proven very useful to me; but his family connections are even more useful.

Have you ever wondered where he gets his nickname from?"

"I can't say I lose any sleep over it," replied Fear nonplussed.

MacPherson uncoiled like a spring from the chair, strode across the splintered floorboards and ripped Johnny's navy blue shirt wide open to reveal a tattoo of a Great White Shark emblazoned across his chest.

"You see friend Johnny is a gypsy, and when I said his family connections would come in very handy to us I meant his true family…the Romani. For it will be them who will help us dissipate our ill-gotten gains through a thousand untraceable channels once the project is completed," and with that MacPherson retreated towards the warmth of the fire.

"You're clever, MacPherson, I'll give you that. So where did the Gypsy connection come from?" asked Fear, clearly fascinated.

"My late wife Dominique was from the French branch of Johnny's family, and, as you can see, Mr Fear, I like to make the most of my family connections," said MacPherson, barking out a harsh laugh that was soon echoed by Johnny and Vallance.

"Okay, you drag me out to the ancestral home, explain your family tree…so now what?" demanded Fear.

"They are all pieces of the jigsaw that need to be placed together to help us achieve our objective. Lanarkyngs will act as our base for what is about to unfold. But before I go any further, is there anything you want to tell me about your little meeting with our two favourite cops, DCI Rothwell and DS Jenkins?

For a second time Fear's face was engulfed in momentary surprise, but before he could say anything MacPherson curtly turned his one-eyed stare on Vallance and Johnny: "Marty, I want you to complete the vehicle checks and confirm everyone in the field is primed. Johnny, can you make sure all the equipment is fit for purpose and good to go?"

"Nae bother, boss," answered Vallance while The Shark flashed a sugary smile: "My pleasure, cuz!"

As their footsteps receded down the corridor MacPherson turned his attention back to Fear: "Before you ask, it wasn't Charlie who told me. But suffice it to say I don't expect any more problems from either Rothwell or Jenkins. And in any case, how is my lovely daughter?" asked MacPherson, the edge in his voice clear.

His mind spinning, Fear paused. Should he come clean with The Cyclops and let him know exactly what Rothwell and Jenkins had been up to and the danger Charlie was in or play ball as if all was well?

He was torn by the dilemma, because the uncomfortable truth that he had begun to realise had been gradually seeping through him, was that he liked The Cyclops almost as much as he despised Rothwell and Jenkins.

That in turn meant that his world was upside down. In The Regiment everything was black and white, but in the world of The Cyclops it was grey, and the bottom line for Fear was that his gut instinct was that Rothwell and Jenkins may have been the law; but they were not serving it by kidnapping an innocent.

He needed more time to come to terms with the situation revolving around Charlie before deciding where to throw in his lot: 'Stall,' said the voice in his head.

Then Fear heard his own voice lie and he felt sick: "I don't know, is the simple truth to that question, MacPherson, and if you don't mind I'd like to keep Charlie separate from all of this."

"Very well. In any case you will have no option in that regard because zero hour is now upon us. Now, to business. One of the big advantages in using Lanarkyngs as our base is that, in addition to affording secrecy, it also provides space and storage. We have the use of the estate garages, such as they remain, and they have been very useful in keeping the vehicle we will be using on this job under wraps."

"So if zero hour is almost upon us, isn't it time you told me exactly what this job I know jack-shit about is?" demanded Fear.

"Tomorrow we are going to pull off THE biggest Heist in British history. The target is Glasgow Airport and £40 million in untraceable notes from military and tourist stops across Europe," said MacPherson as matter-of-factly as if he'd been reading out football results from his Sunday paper.

This time Fear laughed out loud: "Tell me what are we gonna be using…Sherman-bleedin'-tanks?"

"Credit me with some intelligence, Mr Fear, please, if you don't mind. The plan is to get in and out in plain sight without being seen."

"How? Every airport in the UK is on high alert, especially Glasgow after that fiasco of a bomb attack a few years back – it's like bloody Fort Knox! No way, it just can't be done!" replied Fear scornfully.

MacPherson smiled tolerantly and stood up: "Of course it can if we are not who we appear. Why don't you follow me?"

He led the way out through the ruined building and across a yard at the back. A stable block had been converted into a double garage, and MacPherson opened the doors and held out his arm to usher Fear forward.

The vicious bite of the cold damp that hit them came almost as much of a shock as the sharp bright light that burnished the area beyond.

But it was what occupied the space 20 feet in front of him that really shocked him.

For there, in pristine condition, was a parked ambulance.

"As you now see, Mr Fear, my plan is not as ridiculous as you believed. You of all people should know that when you're a member of the Emergency Services no-one asks any questions, you are invisible…yet in plain sight." Then MacPherson strode over to the gleaming vehicle parked just in front of them, pirouetted, held out his hands and said: "Checkmate."

Fear shook his head in disbelief.

45

As Fear attempted to regain his composure and reclaim his jaw from the stone floor, Vallance strode round from the other side of the ambulance.

"Where's the pain, Mr Fear?" he asked sarcastically, before erupting into a grating laugh.

Fear's eyebrows shot up involuntarily, and as he glanced at The Cyclops he saw that he was being studied by that disconcerting lopsided stare MacPherson used when he was tilting his head to the right to apply all the viewing power of his only eye.

"Ten out of ten for imagination, MacPherson, but it's going to take a lot more than a bogus ambulance and a fake crew to make this happen."

"Absolutely, but if you follow me then you will see that there is indeed a lot more to it than meets the eye…which is the whole point to our little enterprise," and then MacPherson jabbed an index finger round behind the ambulance.

As they arced the vehicle Fear immediately felt the welcome warmth blasting from the industrial heaters situated beyond it, and to his amazement he saw that the area was filled with a couple of rows of seats, while a table, desk and big screen were also already set up.

At the front of the two rows of moulded chairs sat Johnny The Shark and another slight middle-aged man who Fear thought he recognised but couldn't quite place.

"Look, I've reserved the best seat in the house for you, Mr Fear," said MacPherson as he gestured for him to take the chair next to The Shark. But before he could sit, two other men – to Fear's amazement fully decked out in fire-fighters' uniforms – filed out of a side door and took up seats in the second row, where they were immediately greeted by the man he couldn't quite place.

"Awright, boys? How yous doin', eh? Yous look real purty in yer uniforms!" the man said, before exploding into a grating laugh that disintegrated into a prolonged smoker's cough.

But MacPherson was determined to keep a tight rein on things: "Settle down, Williams. Glad to see you both, boys; no problems getting here, Andy?"

"Nae bother, boss, we were careful. Anyways, no one is going to be too worried about a Demolition Van coming calling at a place like...this," replied Andy, who Fear put in his mid-thirties.

"Excellent. It's good to see you've got into your fatigues and are ready to go. Now, I realise everyone knows what he's doing but, for the benefit of Mr Fear, we'll just go over it one last time." Then MacPherson sat down at the table, like a director at a dress rehearsal. He flicked a remote control at the screen, and a picture of what appeared to be a Fire Station flashed up.

It was then that it hit Fear just how much planning had gone into 'the project' and the inescapable fact that he had been deliberately left in the dark until the very last moment.

"Okay, what we have up on the screen is a Fire Station; but not just any Fire Station – it's Bridge of Allan Fire Station and it's special because it is staffed by 'the retained'. Who are the retained, I hear you ask? They are professional firefighters who have full-time employment outside the fire service but respond to emergency calls within their local areas as required and work to the Retained Duty System. In Scotland, of the 8,500 firefighters we have, around 32 per cent are retained and are summoned to their local fire station by a radio pager – or bleeper, as you might call it."

MacPherson paused for a quick mouthful from a bottle of mineral water strategically placed on the table next to him.

"I'm delighted to say that Andy and Bobby here are two proud members of the crew of seven retained firefighters who regularly risk their lives to keep the good people of Bridge of Allan safe in their houses every night. But sadly tomorrow morning that protection will be removed while they are otherwise engaged."

MacPherson paused for effect and Fear wondered just how much each member of the assembled cast knew about the Heist that was obviously only hours from being sprung.

"Okay, Marty, you're going to be running this side of things, so if you don't mind can you run over one final time what you, Andy and Bobby are going to get up to?" asked The Cyclops, smiling.

"Sure, boss. As you know, the bleepers will start going off all over Scotland as all the retained boys start to get call-outs for fires they will never find, thanks to oor wee friend at the Barras. While mayhem is erupting in every fire station in Scotland our brave boys will be summoned to the B of A station for an emergency call-out and once they get there they'll be heading oot on the road to Gargunnock for a... bogus barn fire. When they arrive I'll be waiting and then it'll be a case o' mutiny on the Bounty, a quick change o' captain and we'll be gid to go, boss!"

"Anything you want to add to that, Andy? You'll be driving," MacPherson asked.

"It'll be kids' play, Mr MacPherson; the watch manager is a pussy – a dentist who loves playin' the hero and claimin' he's savin' lives at all these wife-swappin' parties he loves to boast about. Well, if he lives tae tell the story he's gonna have somethin' far more interestin' to bore his swinger freends wi'!" And at that the room exploded in laughter that even Fear couldn't fail to join in.

****

MacPherson filled the glass with whisky and passed it to Fear, who hesitated momentarily before taking it.

"I think you'll enjoy this one. 'The 1974', a one-off release specially selected by the Master Distiller at the nearby Deanston Distillery. Matured for 37 years in Oloroso sherry casks with only 102 bottles ever produced. The integrity of this beauty is, quite simply, extraordinary."

"Mind putting a splash of water in it first, MacPherson?" asked Fear and was duly obliged from a small crystal jug that, like the bottle of The 1974 and the two glasses, had mysteriously appeared on the old desk.

As he took a sip from the dark liquid MacPherson regaled Fear with some tasting notes: "The nose is sweet leather with toffee and subtle notes of sherry. While..." MacPherson paused to take a draft, before continuing after an elongated sigh of pleasure: "On the palate luxurious layers of vanilla, cream caramels and honey are balanced with rich oak, sumptuous fruit and exquisite maltiness; and all from a little distillery just along the Teith that was once a cotton mill."

Enjoying his own moment to savour, Fear found himself joining in the songs of praise for The 1974: "Aye, there's no doubt you get a whisper of the sherry from the barrels..."

But then before he waxed even more lyrical, the absurdity of the moment they were now 'enjoying', coupled with his internal self-immolation over Charlie's capture, caused Fear's temper to flare: "This is ludicrous, MacPherson; here we are savouring malt whisky just hours before you hope to pull off one of the biggest robberies ever in the UK. You're barking, bleeding mad."

"Perhaps," replied MacPherson sanguinely, staring into the flames of the peat fire: "But if everything wasn't in place by now there would be no point at all in what we'll be trying to 'pull off', as you put it, tomorrow. So we are enjoying this moment for a reason…Ludovic Fear…and that is because I need to be able to satisfy myself, one last time, that I can trust you when it matters most," concluded MacPherson flatly.

"Look, MacPherson, it's not me you should be worrying about, but our two copper friends," snapped Fear.

The Cyclops smiled serenely: "As I said before, they have been taken care of, and now all that matters is that we have you 100 per cent on the job in hand because, Mr Fear, you, cousin Johnny and I will be crewing the ambulance tomorrow. To be fair to you, Ludovic, you've come through every test I've set you but tomorrow will be different."

46

FEAR racked his mind for a way out, trying desperately not to convey any trace of his inner turmoil. He shook his head dismissively: "Never mind me, MacPherson. I'm assuming we have inside help on this one?"

"We do indeed. I have what I would call an expendable asset inside, thanks to an acquaintance you'll know from your time spent at Her Majesty's pleasure," answered MacPherson caustically.

"Jamieson…I knew he'd be in on this somehow. Fingers in a lot of pies, I guess?"

"You guess right. I think of him as a spider sitting at the centre of his web, parcelling up flies for later use."

"Well, he delivered me," Fear said grimly.

"And that, Ludovic, is something we can both be grateful for." MacPherson raised his glass slightly.

"I'm not sure I'd have let him play me like that a second time around. But look, I'm here, and that should tell you everything you need to know about my commitment to the cause. But I can tell you this for nothing: once this is done and I've got my cut I'm gone, so don't get any ideas about long-term employment."

"We'll see, shall we?" MacPherson smiled.

Fear paused.

"So when do we spring into operation?"

"3am. You'll have time to get your head down. We have bunk beds installed in a room along the corridor, that's almost…fit for purpose in terms of getting some shut-eye. But before you get to catch some sleep, I need to know…is there anything you want to tell me or, indeed, ask of me?"

The question surprised Fear, but again after another sip of The 1974 he pushed his dilemma to the back of his mind. "Actually there is. How the fuck did you come to inherit a place like Lanarkyngs?"

A trace of what appeared to be melancholy seemed to seep from MacPherson, and his lopsided single-eyed stare was applied to Fear almost as if The Cyclops was checking if he was being sincere.

Deciding that he was, MacPherson began: "It's a bit of a sad story, best told in a dark suit, as is so often the case with these old country piles. In the case of Lanarkyngs it all dates back to a road accident in 1927. The estate had been in MacPherson hands for almost 140 years when it happened. My grandfather and his wife were returning to Lanarkyngs when he lost control of the car and it skidded over a 20-foot embankment and ended up in Loch Lubnaig. Sadly my grandmother, Ellen, was pinned in the car, and despite his efforts my grandfather couldn't free her and tragically she perished. From then on he associated Lanarkyngs with the tragedy and was never to stay in the Castle again. Unused and unloved, it fell into neglect, and when the old man passed in the 70s it fell to my father's elder brother, Simon, who was more interested in the casinos of London and his sailing club than restoring our ancestral home," concluded MacPherson, his gaze lost in the flames.

"A sad story all right, but I'm guessin' there's plenty more to come…?" asked Fear, leaving the question hanging in the peat-filled air.

MacPherson smiled wanly: "Ultimately my uncle decided he was going to have it demolished, despite its category B listed status. Anyway, before he could go through with it he too perished in a motorcycle accident on the Invertrossachs Road, on the way to his beloved Loch Venachar sailing club…people said that the curse of the MacPhersons had struck again," said The Cyclops, wincing before he returned to the comfort of his malt.

Despite the obvious sense of maudlin that seemed to be enveloping MacPherson, Fear couldn't help himself: "But you being a bastard, how does it all end up coming your way… Obadiah?" he asked, unwilling to stop a sarcastic emphasis resting on MacPherson's newly-discovered Christian name.

"My father, Captain Hugh MacPherson, only had one legitimate child and I'm afraid, as you now know, I was born on the wrong side of the sheets. Sadly he died of lung cancer when he was in his early 40s, and all my mother was left with were empty promises and the old lodge house; he had given the castle and life-rent of the lodge house to his wife Joanna…" At that MacPherson threw up his hands in frustration: "Ultimately my mother, just like my grandfather, died of a broken heart, penniless in a council house down in the village of Doune. But she never let me forget who my father was, and nor could I ever dismiss my childhood memories. God, I had some good times…Bill the Clydesdale Pony and Fergus the Sheltie. The huge shining black Rolls Royce and an Armstrong Siddeley Sapphire 234 with its V-shaped radiator grille and silver Sphinx motif that flew magnificently upon it…" MacPherson shut his eye and slipped into a sullen silence, his mind clearly replaying sepia-dimmed memories from his childhood.

Fear eyed MacPherson in disbelief at these revelations.

But The Cyclops had not finished and after taking another mouthful of whisky his voice, taking on a wistful timbre, broke into life once more: "Aah the 234, God how I loved that car! Manufactured between 1955 and 1958 with a four-cylinder 2290cc engine and a manual four-speed gearbox. Only 803 were produced! Did you know they called it the 100mph car for the man who liked high performance?" MacPherson laughed ruefully.

Fear shook his head: "So, I'm just guessin', but this little tale of the unexpected tends to make me think that, somehow, you'll be using some of the funds from the Heist to restore Lanarkyngs to its former glories?"

"Eventually, indeed I will. I want, almost more than anything, that this wonderful place is secured for the future." Then he fished out what appeared to be an old photograph from his inside jacket pocket and handed it to Fear.

The latter examined it intently. It was an old photo of a young lady, maybe around 20, who sat regally on a grassy mound in a crisp white blouse and dark three-quarter length woollen skirt in the forefront of the castle itself, its full majestic glory proudly brooding in the background.

The gnarled presence of the old chestnut tree that Fear had noticed to the left of Lanarkyngs' castellated entrance on his arrival added an almost haunting quality to the time-faded picture.

"Is this your mother?" he asked.

"Yes, taken in 1964, around six months after I was born. Look how happy she was, it radiates from the picture – my father had promised her the earth, promised her Lanarkyngs, but..."

"He never delivered," said Fear, finishing the sentence for him.

"So you see I want to deliver on that promise to my mother. God bless her, she never wanted to leave this place, and one day I want to bring her back here and have her buried next to my father where she belongs. And then, of course, I want to pass it on to Charlie – Charlie and her husband and family. You see for me, Mr Fear, family is everything, which is why I take very seriously who my daughter is seeing…"

But before MacPherson could finish his monologue the mixture of rage and guilt that had been steadily threatening to burst the inner dam of Fear's resolve snapped: "For fuck's sake, MacPherson, just shut up about your precious Lanarkyngs and your bloody family tree. You can forget all about the Heist, it's never gonna happen…Rothwell and Jenkins have Charlie. They've got her in a safe house somewhere," he burst out, his eyes locking on MacPherson.

The Cyclops stared at him unseeing: "Repeat!" he demanded.

"Rothwell sent me a text from her mobile telling me to turn up at the Castle and there he was. Basically he wants me to set you up in return for Charlie…" Fear's words faded into silence, but there was no doubting the conclusion they drew.

For the first time since he had met MacPherson, he saw The Cyclops was visibly at a loss over what to do, and he began to knead at twin points on either side of his forehead with his index finger and thumb.

"Christ…that means they've taken care of McColl as well…bastards," and at that MacPherson sprung to his feet and launched his whisky glass into the peaty flames. They sizzled with renewed delight at his sacrificial offering.

Then, his one eye blazing with momentary madness, he turned round and sprang across the room. He grabbed Fear, clamping both hands around his neck and ramming him against a crumbling damp stained wall: "Why the fuck didn't you tell me sooner? This is your fault, Fear, you've dragged Charlie into all of this…"

But before he could complete his rant Fear forced his forearms upwards, breaking MacPherson's grip and followed up with a right hook to the solar plexus that dropped The Cyclops like a stone.

Down on all fours, MacPherson gasped for air that refused to come as above him Fear towered unforgivingly: "Listen to me, MacPherson. I've told you this, despite the fact it's going to cost me my son and my liberty, because I love Charlie and knowing that even if we can get her out of this in one piece my chances of sharing anything with her are gone. So don't take your bleedin' anger out on me."

As MacPherson's rasping slowly subsided, Fear took a couple of steps back and sat down on his seat as if nothing had happened: "Don't worry about your pride, MacPherson, I've taken down bigger units than you with that shot. There are a lot of nerves just below your sternum, and when you land the shot the diaphragm goes into spasm, and you're left without a breath and in a helluva lot of pain…the good thing is that you're so fucked you're gonna listen to me. Because while you were bleating on about your project I've been trying to work out how we can get Charlie out alive and maybe, just maybe, save our own skins."

MacPherson hauled himself up onto his feet and sat back down heavily at the desk: "All right, Fear, you have my undivided attention now…so tell me just how are we going to save Charlie?"

47

Jock Shirley checked his watch for the umpteenth time just as he heard the footsteps coming from behind him. "Shit," he muttered at the prospect of McNulty catching him out again, before quickly slipping his *Racing Times* under the logbook just as his supervisor reached the reception desk.

McNulty span the reception desk chair around, clasping its arms with either hand and eyeballing his guard: "What the fuck's the matter with you, Shirley? It don't matter how many times you look at yer fake Lanzarote Omega you're still gonna have three hours to the end of yer shift. Now get your lazy arse off my seat, make your spot checks round the warehouse and earn your fuckin' wage for once in your miserable, snivelling life."

As McNulty released his grip on the chair, Shirley jumped to his feet and touched his hat respectfully: "Sorry, gaffer, been a long night, what with the delivery tae store in the reserve and all, and the wee wan is teethin' so I got fuck all kip yesterday, tae be honest I'm a bit buggered, gaffer. But I'll get crackin…"

"Make sure you do, Shirley, 'cause the next time I catch you lookin' at yer watch I'll put you on report. Do you have any fuckin' idea of the value of the consignment we have stored inside this warehouse right now?" demanded McNulty.

"Didn't figure it was any of my business, gaffer," Shirley replied, hanging his head in suitable supplication.

McNulty's eyes continued to sear him before he spat: "40 million, that's how much we're keepin' cosy in the vault tonight. So you make your fuckin' checks, and make sure there is nothing out of place, cos if there is I will personally fry you, Shirley, and you can forget ever placing another bleedin' bet on the GGs again."

Shirley walked off, heading for the first electronic perimeter checkpoint. A swipe of his identity card would confirm it was secure, which in turn would show up on McNulty's control computer.

The warehouse sat adjacent to Glasgow Airport's most eastern runway and ensured that when the British Airways Boeing 747 eight-freighter landed, its lucrative contents could be bussed under armed guard straight to the ramp door at the rear of the warehouse without the public's gaze ever falling on it.

But as he reached the second checkpoint and swiped his card, waiting for the reassuring bleep that it had been registered on McNulty's command and control terminal, a bead of sweat dropped onto the tiled floor below Shirley… then a vicious smile swept across the security guard's worn features…because payback was coming.

He checked his watch: '3.54am, six minutes to go, before all hell breaks loose. Time to get moving,' he told himself. If he didn't make it in time then he could expect McNulty to bawl him out over the warehouse intercom and shame him once again in front of the rest of his colleagues…but that would be the last time he ever did.

At recognition of that comforting fact Shirley muttered with a grin: "Fuckin' little Hitler, you've got it comin'."

The security guard tried to quicken his pace, but the arthritis in his knee – a legacy of his years spent as a Junior footballer with Pollock, and a talent that had never been quite good enough to make it in the senior ranks – stabbed painfully. As always, it was a struggle getting round the circuit of checkpoints to time.

50 yards short of checkpoint Charlie he heard McNulty's grating voice spout out through the Tannoy system: "Guard Shirley, you are 25 seconds late. Please complete your perimeter check then see me immediately."

Gasping for air, Shirley swiped his card, bent down, rolled his uniform trouser up his left leg and pulled the claw hammer out of his sock.

Then with a precise blow he smashed the glass panel on the fire alarm three yards away from the checkpoint.

As the fire alarm erupted Shirley pulled out a mobile from his pocket and punched in a one-word text: 'Go'.

"Fuck you, McNulty," spat Jock Shirley and raised a single index finger in the air at the CCTV camera.

****

The powerful 260bhp engine of the Scania P94DB was drowned by the wailing of the Fire Tender's siren as it roared past the main terminal building and arrived at the security gate leading to the road running adjacent to the East runway.

As it slowed to a stop at the security barrier the guard stepped out of his hut: "Nae bother, mate, I can hear the alarm from here," and with a thumbs up he pressed the barrier control button and stood back as it lifted.

Inside the Fire Tender's cabin a lustrous almost Mexican moustache twitched into a smile of gratitude: "¡Gracias, amigo!" muttered the driver through a broad smile and the Fire Tender shot through.

No sooner had the vehicle sped off than an ambulance arrived in its slipstream, and as it drew to a stop the driver's window slid down, the jet-haired driver leaned out over his windowsill and said conversationally: "Sorry, pal, control are saying there's been some kind of accident at the east warehouse, better get out there pronto!"

The security guard laughed: "Fuck me, you boys are on yer toes this mornin'!" As he completed his greeting the guard realised there was something mesmerising about the driver's right eye, even from behind a pair of dark shades.

"Cheers, pal! We better get the wagon out there before these firefighters make a bad situation worse. You know what they're like, fuckin' cowboys, by the time we get to the warehoose they'll be needin' stretchers!"

The guard smiled: "On you go boys, nae botha!" and at that, with a wave of gratitude from the driver, the ambulance sped off.

MacPherson turned to Fear: "Time you fed PC Plod a titbit!"

Fear nodded curtly and quickly typed in a text then read it out: "Turn on *Today*. Text you when and where minute I have it."

"Excellent, now send it," said MacPherson, his grip on the steering wheel tightening.

"It's gone. Christ, I hope this is going to work," said Fear letting go an audible exhalation of breath.

"Look, I can't raise McColl, so Rothwell has obviously taken care of him, and now he has Charlie he holds all the aces. But he has no reason to suspect you of any…subterfuge. You've promised him my head on a plate. That's enough to keep him dangling. It's time to focus on the job in hand, Mr Fear. We'll get to Rothwell when we come out the other side," concluded MacPherson and refocused his gaze on the looming depot.

The warehouse was a quarter of a mile away from the runway entrance gate, and through the reinforced glass panes of the security reception windows McNulty could see the Fire Tender speeding his way.

Checking his panel he realised that the fire alarm had been activated from the same checkpoint Charlie sector that Shirley had been late for. He grabbed his walkie-talkie and immediately snapped out a command to his subordinate: "Guard Shirley, come in, I need a report on the status of Charlie sector immediately."

He was met with silence.

Turning to his right he called over another guard.

"Lawson, get out to Charlie sector and see what's goin' on there. That's where the fire alarm was activated and where that lazy fool Shirley just clocked in. Now I can't raise him on the walkie-talkie and the CCTV camera has gone down! Pronto, if you don't mind..."

No sooner had Lawson gone than the Fire Tender drew up outside the warehouse doors, and a firefighter jumped out of his cabin and strode into Reception.

McNulty walked round to the front of his desk and met the driver with a smile: "Sorry, pal, I don't know what's happening, other than there's been a fire alarm activation in Charlie sector, at the rear of the building."

As he completed his summation a look of incredulity spread across the supervisor's angular face: the firefighter had removed a revolver from his tunic pocket.

Suddenly, the firefighter threw the handgun into the air and they both watched as it somersaulted over and over; but as it came down he grabbed the barrel and smashed the pistol handle off the side of McNulty's head. The supervisor crumpled onto the ceramic entrance tiles, out cold before he had even hit them.

At his back the Fire Tender had already reversed to a stop just yards away from the entrance, blocking any view of what was going on inside from the security checkpoint a quarter of a mile away.

Vallance took charge of the control panel, shutting down its CCTV cameras while his crew filed in and split into two, three making for the restroom, where several of the warehouse staff would be enjoying a break and the others immediately heading down a corridor to the left of the building.

Phase One had been completed and control of the Warehouse achieved. Vallance pulled out his mobile and tapped out a quick text: 'Boys on way to U'.

****

The ambulance screeched to a stop beside the ramp at the warehouse's rear door, where Shirley opened the doors.

MacPherson turned it around and reversed to the entrance, Johnny The Shark jumped out of its rear and Fear sprang out of the passenger seat, all three immaculate in their pristine green ambulance technician's suits, with baseball caps in matching lime green pulled down tight and wrap-around sun glasses covering their eyes.

As they entered the opened doorway Shirley stood transfixed, unsure what would happen now he had played his part. His moment of uncertainty was soon ended as The Cyclops grabbed him by his tunic and rammed him up against a concrete wall.

"Guard Shirley, I presume?" He was answered with a hesitant nod.

"So where is the vault?" demanded MacPherson.

"It's in the basement. But…I'm…sorry…there's a… well…fly in the ointment…the codes have been changed…" stuttered the quaking Shirley.

48

BEFORE Shirley could finish he felt the cold steel of a Makarov rammed up against the underside of his chin: "Think very hard before you continue – your next answer will decide if you live or die. Who has the new code and how quickly can we get it?" demanded The Cyclops, his calm beginning to fray.

"The only person who knows the new code is my supervisor, Terry McNulty," replied Shirley, his voice a terrified whisper.

"I hope so for your sake, Guard Shirley…You were paid good money to get us into that fuckin' vault. So where's this McNulty?"

"He'll be in the foyer with the fire brigade," replied Shirley, his eyes wide with terror.

Looking over his shoulder MacPherson was about to bark an order out but Johnny The Shark had already read his mind and was calling Vallance: "You got the supervisor, McNulty, there with you mate? We need him here pronto, the codes have changed, and he's the only one with the new ones."

Even yards away MacPherson and Fear both heard Vallance's reply from the other end: "On my way."

Fear checked his watch and shook his head ruefully: "This is costing us time we don't have! How long is it going to take to get Terry Fuckwit to the vault?"

"Six minutes," answered the terrified security guard.

MacPherson removed the Makarov from under Shirley's chin and flicked it towards the corridor to their left: "Take us to the vault…now!"

Moments later they arrived at the reinforced steel doors. Fear checked his watch: "That's eight minutes, 39 seconds since we arrived. This is fuckin' dodgy!"

But he had no sooner finished his sentence than the noise of boots slapping on concrete resonated from down the corridor, and Vallance came into sight, pushing a dishevelled and blood-spattered figure ahead of him.

As they arrived MacPherson barked at Vallance: "Who've you left on the doors? What about the rest of the staff?"

Vallance inclined his head slightly: "Just got the call on the walkie-talkie on the way to you…four more guards gagged and bound by three of Andy's lads while he has stayed on the doors just in case. But all quiet…"

"Excellent! Supervisor McNulty, I presume? I have one question for you. Give me the wrong answer and…" The Cyclops lifted the Mkarov and pointed it at McNulty's head: "You're a dead man."

McNulty's features were frozen in fear as MacPherson placed the barrel of the handgun against his forehead: "What's the new code for the vault? And don't even think about playing for time."

"0001967," he stammered.

MacPherson smiled: "Set by a Celtic supporter to commemorate the Lisbon Lions' finest hour? Very good." Then MacPherson nodded to The Shark: "Over to you, Johnny."

But as Johnny approached the first of a set of double doors Shirley shouted: "Stop!" and tried to catch Johnny by the arm.

As everyone's eyes turned on him he blurted out: "It's a trap. The two security doors are laser alarmed. If you open the first and then try and open the second before it's shut, all hell will break loose. McNulty's fuckin' settin' you up."

"All of which means that we can place no trust in anything you say, Mr McNulty...wouldn't you agree?" asked MacPherson, his one eye narrowed to a slit.

"No, no it was an honest mistake...I ...wasn't thinking straight. Shirley's right about the doors: the first has to shut before you can activate the second, which is opened by a separate password," blurted out McNulty.

From behind him Fear rapped: "Problem is, how can we believe you, man?" Then he turned to MacPherson and added: "We don't have time to fuck about here, so I brought a little persuasion with me for just such a case of...stage fright." He turned to Vallance and Johnny: "Pin him to the fuckin' wall."

Unnoticed up to that point, in his right hand Fear had been carrying a small jerrycan and he deftly unscrewed the top and rammed it into McNulty's guts: "Listen to me, I'm about to douse you in petrol, you snivelling little arsehole, so you better convince me everything else you say from now on is the truth or..." then Fear slipped an orange plastic lighter from his green suit and flicked the flame on.

It was too much for McNulty. He yelped and started struggling furiously, but that didn't stop the icy chill of the fuel showering him.

Having emptied the content of the jerrycan, Fear stood back: "Okay you prick, spit it out. Fuck up and, okay, we get caught; but you'll enjoy a death you couldn't imagine in your worst nightmares...what's it to be, shit-for-brains?" he demanded.

"Okay, okay I get it, I'll tell you everything...no shit...I swear it on my weans' lives."

MacPherson paced forward and grabbed the supervisor's throat and rammed his head against the wall: "And the password is?"

"Stein!" screeched the terrified McNulty.

"Of course, how very appropriate," laughed The Cyclops at the use of Celtic's immortal former manager Jock Stein's surname: "I very much hope for your sake it is," replied MacPherson almost amicably then he turned to The Shark: "Okay, Johnny, so it's 0001967 to open the first set of doors then we all move through, wait for it to close behind us and you key in Stein in the second pad and we're in. Is that right, Mr McNulty?" asked MacPherson, reinforcing the pressure on the supervisor's throat until he started to gag from its constriction.

"Yes…yes, that's it," he finally coughed. MacPherson nodded to Johnny to activate the first set of doors.

As the keypad completed its final bleep on the last digit, the bulletproof glass panel slid open, and they all walked through, then waited for the door to close behind them, which it did smoothly.

But as Johnny reached out to key in the password for the second door, Fear grabbed him by the shoulder: "Wait a minute, matey. Our friend didn't say whether it was initial cap on Stein or all lowercase."

He let the question hang in the air as all heads once again turned to McNulty and Vallance grabbed a handful of hair and snapped his head back. The supervisor needed no further persuasion:

"Capital 'S', then all lower case, I swear it. You need to tap the 's' twice to make it a capital…"

"Now how the fuck would I have known that without you being so bleedin' helpful…nice one, matey," murmured The Shark and they all held their breath as he keyed in the password. The second door slid open to the sound of a relieved silence.

"We're fuckin' in!" boomed Vallance, as the advance party walked into the vault.

MacPherson immediately checked the CCTV cameras mounted on the four corners of the vault, making sure that the information on the security systems Shirley had been enlisted to provide had allowed Vallance to shut down the internal surveillance system.

They were all dead, and permitting himself a brief smile as he swept the room's rows of silvery metallic deposit boxes with an avaricious gaze, MacPherson turned towards McNulty: "Now we are in, Mr McNulty – or can I call you Terry? What's the procedure to get out...I presume it's a mirror image of the way in?" he rapped.

McNulty nodded his head in the affirmative.

"Excellent. Now I have some good news and some bad news, Mr McNulty. Which would you like first?" The Cyclops asked peaceably.

The supervisor's fear-flecked eyes widened into saucers before he stuttered: "I dunno what you mean?"

But MacPherson had lost patience: "We'll go for the good news first, I think. You're not going to be burned alive. The bad news is..." His head tilted towards Vallance in his peculiar lopsided stare: "You must die anyway."

The words had barely escaped his mouth when Vallance whipped out his Glock and pumped lead into the supervisor's forehead. The back of McNulty's head exploded onto the wall and his corpse slithered onto the concrete...a dead weight.

MacPherson immediately turned to Shirley: "That's what happens to people who cross me, Mr Shirley." Then he turned to Williams: "Get the jemmies out. The ten big deposit boxes to the left are full of the military money. £40 million in used notes just waiting for us, boys...we clear them first and if things are good we can see what the shit is like in the other boxes." Then MacPherson looked over towards Williams and nodded his head.

"Nae bother, Mr MacPherson, boss mawn," nodded the snout and started handing out the jemmies to Johnny, Fear, Vallance and Shirley.

Johnny was first to spring into action, attacking the first big steel box with manic glee. Eventually the box sprung slightly from its setting, and he forced the sharp side of the jemmy in and levered it out until there was enough of the container hanging out to rip open with his hands.

As it shot out and landed on the ceramic-tiled floor it tipped over onto its side with a metallic clunk, and its contents spilled onto the shiny floor.

Used notes in mixed bundles of £100s, £50s, £20s and £10s.

"Eu-fuckin'-reka!" shouted The Shark.

Involuntarily five pairs of eyes came to rest on MacPherson, whose face was momentarily lit by a salacious smile, which disappeared almost as quickly as it had broken.

Then The Cyclops checked his watch: "Okay, it's 0415hrs, boys. The dayshift are due at 0600hrs but we need to be gone long before then. Work as if your lives depended on it; fill the bags my brave boys, fill the bags and let's get the hell out of here."

49

THE black plastic bindings bit into Charlie's wrists while the adhesive tape that clamped her mouth shut was seeping a nauseous, almost chemical taste into her mouth that made her gag as she attempted to swallow the vomit back down.

Overnight she had remained bound to a chair positioned in the bay window of the third floor flat's substantial lounge. As the new day dawned her eyes scanned the dramatic view across the Forth Valley out towards the meandering sparkling River Forth and beyond to the distant Ochil Hills that were now bathed golden in the first of the early morn rays.

Judging by the slight crust in her eyes she must have slept at some point during the night, but Charlie certainly didn't feel like that had been the case. By contrast, the snoring coming from Jenkins, who lay curled up on a large two piece brown velvet couch, provided ample proof that her captor had not been troubled by any qualms over his current engagement.

Jenkins' rest was interrupted by a text alert. He grunted and sat up, ran a hand though his dishevelled dark strands, wiped his eyes clear, grabbed his mobile off the coffee table and read its screen.

His back to Charlie, Jenkins said two words: "At last," and then stood up and strode over to her. Hunkering down opposite, he snatched her chin between his thumb and forefinger, forcing her sleepy hazel eyes to look his way.

"Well, Dusty, looks like things are finally moving and your boyfriend is going to help us bring down your old man once and for all. Jeez, that must be a tough prospect for you...daddy's little girl!" He patted her on the cheek and dissolved into a vicious laugh.

Then to Charlie's surprise he almost tenderly peeled the tape back from her mouth.

His predatory eyes devoured her: "C'mon, sweetheart, you must have some clue what's going on...look we're gonna know soon enough what's on the menu, so why don't you do us all a favour and spill? Look at it this way: anything you tell me now could save lives...'cause I bet whatever your old man is up to he ain't doin' it packin' a peashooter."

Mustering all the scorn she could sum up, Charlie snapped: "Look, I've told you and your boss already I don't know what my dad or Ludovic Fear are up to. I haven't seen Ludo since that night at the pub and as for my dad..."

But before she could continue, Jenkins seized on the crumb she had let slip: "Oh dear, Dusty, trouble in paradise is there?" Then he undid the ties binding her to the chair, grabbed Charlie's right arm and pulled his captive to her feet before propelling Charlie onto the settee.

She perched precariously half-on and half-off the top of the seat, but Jenkins quickly closed the small space between them, his rapacious intent almost dripping from him and grabbed her by the shoulders. He pulled Charlie up until her face was less than an inch from his.

"God, you don't know how long I've waited for this," he said, his foul breath coming in excited blasts. Charlie turned her head in disgust, but he forced her face back to his and clamped his lips on hers.

Despite Charlie's desperate attempts to pull away, Jenkins' lips remained locked on hers for what seemed an eternity until finally he withdrew.

"Mmm, the appetiser was worth the wait; but now I'm really looking forward to the main course," he grinned voraciously, and then Jenkins shoved her onto the settee.

Lying on her back, Charlie drew her knees up to her chest and slipped her bound hands down and over her ankles, at the same time slipping the nail file she had secreted inside her gym sock into her bound hands. It was a precaution Charlie had been accustomed to adopting ever since one of her friends had been indecently assaulted by a member of her gym, who subsequently turned out to be an admirer who wouldn't take no for answer.

Surprised by her adroit manoeuvre Jenkins hesitated above her, but the bounds of his self-restraint had well and truly snapped: "Dear Dusty, when this is all over you're gonna need someone to take care of you, when Daddy and soldier boy are banged up doin' lifers, someone who has connections, someone who has a future…"

Then he sat down on the settee next to her: "You know that DCI Rothwell is going all the way to the top and that he will be taking me with him. With Police Scotland there is a whole new world out there for guys like him and me: men who are prepared to take chances. The first time I saw you I knew you had to be mine…" Then once again Jenkins grabbed Charlie by the shoulders and turned her towards him, his eyes shutting as the mounting anticipation grew and his hands began to take on a mind of their own.

Charlie thrust the nail file up with all the power she possessed, ramming it into Jenkins' neck just below his chin and he gasped and jerked in agony.

Crimson burst from him. The nail file had clearly punctured an artery, and as he desperately clasped his hands to the wound, Jenkins fell onto the beige and brown-checked rug that covered the fireside area, frantically attempting to stem the jets of blood spouting from his neck.

As he lay gagging, Charlie stood over him and placed her right foot on his chest: "Judging by the way you're losing blood, I'd say I've hit your carotid artery and your life is now ebbing away. Did you really think that I was some helpless damsel in distress waiting for you to do with me what you wanted?"

Jenkins, his eyes growing glassier with every second, begged for help as the blood pouring from his severed left Carotid started to drown him: "For Chrissakes, call me an ambulance, you mad bitch."

Instead Charlie increased the pressure of her foot on his chest: "Did I tell you that I was a medical student at Glasgow University before I persuaded my dad to let me sing for my supper? So let me tell you what's happening to you, my darling DS Jenkins," and then Charlie knelt down and pulled her hoody sleeve up to look at her watch. "You're already starting to lose consciousness, so it's too late for an ambulance; within two minutes you'll be brain dead. It's the end of the road for you, DS Jenkins, and pretty soon it'll be all over for your boss." Then Charlie smiled sweetly.

"Help me...please," croaked Jenkins, his voice fading to a whisper as ruby red started to seep out of the sides of his mouth.

Charlie bent closer and whispered into his ear: "Sleep tight, lover boy." Then she rifled his pockets until she located his mobile, stood up and walked back over to the bay window, looked out into the breaking dawn and smiled.

Now she had Rothwell exactly where she wanted him and he didn't even know it.

Checking her watch, Charlie saw that she only had 45 minutes to be where she needed to be, yet for a moment she hovered at the window, staring out across the misty Forth Valley. A deep sense of foreboding growing inside her, because she knew that everything hinged on the Airport job…where the two men she loved more than life itself were facing their moment of triumph or disaster.

50

"COME on, Williams, get a move on will you? We need to be out of here pronto," snapped MacPherson, standing at the back of the ambulance and waving his henchman forward.

"By Christ, ne'er realised how heavy a full bag o'loot wid be, sufferin' sodees, but my back is fair loupin," groaned Williams, but as he did so Fear's powerful figure strode towards him and ripped the holdall stuffed full of notes from his shoulders and launched it onto the pile of bags that had already almost filled the rear of the vehicle.

"That's the last of it, MacPherson. Now can we get the hell out of here?" rapped the former soldier.

But before MacPherson could reply, his walkie-talkie crackled into life with the unmistakeable deep rumbling tones of Vallance's voice: "Had Airport control on earlier wantin' to know what's happening and if all's well. Got Shirley to fob them off, told 'em it wiz a false alarm, fuckin' glad we kept him alive, the fact they know him and all, been a lifesaver. He's been fuckin' useful considering the mess he made of the passwords! But they've been back on again demandin' to know when we are clearin' off…they're starting tae get suspicious. Been askin' bout the bleedin' ambulance as well, boss."

"Keep a lid on it, Marty, and make sure that Shirley doesn't start panicking; that's the last bag in the back of the ambulance, and I'm on my way through to see you, so just stay calm and get your boys ready to leave."

"Done," came Vallance's terse reply.

Fear and Johnny, standing just yards away, did not have long to wait for their next set of instruction, as MacPherson turned their way: "Okay, gentlemen, lock her up and take her round to the front, where I will meet you. Williams, I want you in the back with the currency. Understood?"

"Aye, Mr MacPherson, nae bother, like," replied Williams in his usual grovelling manner.

Turning to the rest of the gang MacPherson said: "Now, everyone knows what's expected of them en route to our rendezvous. All polythene gloves must be kept on until I say otherwise. I've got you this far, my boys...you trust me to get you out the other side, don't you?" he demanded, his one-eyed stare searching every face for a hint of doubt or treachery.

There was none and instead they roared: "Yes," in adrenaline-fuelled unison.

"Excellent, now jump to it, boys," growled MacPherson, waving his right hand before him in a sweeping gesture. Then he strode off up the corridor followed by two of the bogus firefighters.

"Well, matey, looks like it's me and you up top in the wagon, just like Butch Cassidy and the Sundance kid, eh, El Agente Grant?" cracked The Shark, laughing lightly and slapping Fear on the back as if he didn't have a care in the world.

"I just hope we don't have the whole of the Bolivian army forming a welcoming party for us around the corner," replied Fear grimly, as he gestured to Williams to clamber onto the bags of cash stuffed in the rear of the ambulance.

"Jist hae faith in The Cyclops and he'll get us hame and dry tae Lanarkyngs," Williams sang out as he made himself comfortable on top of the stacked holdalls."

"Let's just hope we can make it out the Airport alive first," he smiled wanly at Williams and slammed the door shut before making sure it was locked-fast.

As he jumped into the cabin and turned the ignition on Fear swivelled The Shark's way: "Did you know the RV is Lanarkyngs?"

"Makes perfek sense to me, matey. It's derelict, in the middle of Sherwood-bleedin'-forest and nobody knows a poncin' thing about it. Ideal, El Agente Grant, for Robin Hood and his merry men to divvy their loot – in fact bleeding lush, if you ask me."

And for once Fear found no argument with Johnny's logic as they both erupted into nerve-flecked laughter.

****

As MacPherson arrived at the warehouse reception desk he flashed a reassuring thumbs up Shirley's way and followed it up with: "Good job, pal; you've earned every penny keeping these imbeciles from Airport Control at bay, and you will be well rewarded." Then he turned to Vallance: "Okay, Marty, all your firefighters on board, helmets screwed down tight and ready for departure?"

"Aye, boss, champin' at the bit tae get tae."

Then in a rare gesture of warmth MacPherson extended his right hand and shook him warmly by the hand, saying: "Excellent. Well done, Marty, you've done me proud. I'll see you at the rendezvous in approximately one hour." Then MacPherson quickly checked his watch: "That'll be 0625hours? You better get going, my friend," smiled MacPherson.

"Nae bother, boss, take care on the way out."

As Vallance turned to go, MacPherson's voice shouted over his shoulder: "Oh Marty, don't forget this," and lobbed his yellow helmet at his right-hand man.

Then MacPherson turned towards Shirley, smiled benignly and placed a friendly arm around the guard reassuringly. "Okay, Jock, isn't it? All I need is one thing more of you and then we are out of here and all your worries will be taken care of," he said.

"Whit's that, Mr MacPherson, just name it," replied Shirley, clearly relieved that he had redeemed himself from his earlier faux pas with the passwords.

"I need you to call Airport Control and let them know that all is good and that both the fire and ambulance services are standing down and that, as I imagine is standard procedure, you will email them with a routine report on the callout as soon as possible."

"Nae bother," Shirley replied and quickly grabbed the reception desk phone and duly did as he was bid.

Listening intently from the other side of the reception desk, MacPherson smiled as Shirley's flawless deception was completed with the replacing of the phone back in its holder.

"Well done, Jock, you've bought us the time we need to get out of the Airport unchallenged and for that I am eternally grateful. But unfortunately you won't be joining us..." and a look of utter incomprehension enveloped Shirley's gnarled face as MacPherson raised his Makarov.

"You fucked up, Shirley, but if it makes you feel any better, this was only ever going to end one way for you. I'm afraid you would be just too obvious a lead for the Police to follow up. But..." and MacPherson smiled almost balefully at the man he was sentencing to death: "If it's any consolation all your debts will be wiped clear by Jamieson and your wife and weans will be benefiting from an unexpected windfall." Then MacPherson pulled the trigger and watched with cruel detachment as the mix of shock and disbelief on Shirley's face was wiped away by an explosion of gore.

"Too bad," said The Cyclops, reholstering the gun inside his green ambulance overalls and walking out of the warehouse reception.

51

THE ambulance reached the security checkpoint just as Vallance and his crew of firefighters drove off, and the very fact that their confederates had made it back out without a hitch immediately put MacPherson's team at ease.

Fear slipped down through the gears, bringing the ambulance stationary just before the checkpoint barrier, then slid the driver's window down: "Okay, pal, job done, panic over, time to head back to the station for a nice wee cup of cha!"

The guard broke a lazy smile: "Aye, it never ceases to amaze me how they manage to fuck things up so often down the road. Christ they manage about one alarm every ten days, me and the boys have a wee book runnin' tryin' to guess when the next one will be. Must be staffin' the warehouse with a bunch o' bleedin' muppets if you ask me. Ever since they put it oot tae tender and turned it o'er to private firms it's been wan fuck up after another," he concluded, taking his lid off and starting to scratch at the remnants of a once thick chestnut thatch.

Fear kept his features neutral and despite the tension played the game: "So you boys airport staff then, as opposed to Keystone Cops?"

But the guard's ruddy features took on a look of puzzlement: "Hey, don't I know you from somewhere? Your face sure is…familiar."

Fear produced a rueful smile: "That'll be my twin brother; works with Special Branch and spent years working ports and airports. You must have bumped into him at least once or twice…small world, eh?" he said, hoping for the best as he clocked MacPherson starting to ease his handgun out from his green boiler suit.

The guard nodded his head: "Aye, maybees that's it, could a' sworn you resembled someone else I saw recently… anyways, I'll naw hold yeez up any longer or you'll never get that cuppa," and at that he pressed the release button and the red and white hooped barrier shot up.

Fear eased the ambulance clear but it was Johnny who put their feelings into words: "Bugger me…I thought you woz made matey," he bleated.

"You're not the only one."

"For Christ sakes, matey, we've done it! We've just walked off with 40 mill in the back of a soddin' ambulance! I tell you, the first bleed'n thing I'm doin' once we're clear of all this is getting' my season ticket at The Emirates booked, then it's prawn sandwiches and champers for Johnny The Shark every other soddin' Saturday! Up the Arsenal!" he shouted, punching the air in euphoria.

"Très bien, mon ami! Make sure you say Bonjour to Monsieur Wenger pour moi!" laughed MacPherson.

At this Williams started howling at the top of his voice from the rear of the ambulance like a moon-crazed dog.

But while his companions burst into peals of laughter as the relief that they had pulled off the Heist rebounded around the cabin in a shared moment of seismic triumph, Fear was anything but ecstatic: "Problem is that when the balloon goes up there's every chance that our friend Sid the security guard will make me…eventually…we've got blood on our hands, MacPherson, and they won't give up until they've got us all," he muttered, his eyes remaining locked on the road.

"There can be no argument over McNulty. But if you're referring to Shirley, then I'm afraid I had no choice. The first thing any copper will look for is an inside man…just like they did with the Brinks-Mat job and once they have him then we are a house of cards waiting to fold," concluded MacPherson.

"So you had to plug him?"

"I don't tend to bother answering rhetorical questions, Mr Fear." MacPherson grabbed his cell phone and punched in a text.

As he did so Fear couldn't help himself: "Rothwell?"

"In a moment…but first I need to make sure our crash car is alongside and ready…just in case things get sticky."

"Crash car?" asked Fear.

From the other side of the cabin MacPherson was busy checking the passenger side mirror and a smile began to play at either side of his mouth: "Trust me, your patience is about to be rewarded."

Fear glowered at MacPherson but chose to say nothing. As Fear drove the ambulance onto the M8 (Glasgow) Airport flyover, he was startled to glimpse a worryingly familiar navy blue Ford Focus in his rear-view mirror, weaving its way through the traffic catching up fast.

"Fuck it, CID motor coming our way, one up," reported Fear, but MacPherson remained silent.

The Focus drew level with the ambulance and Fear snapped: "You better get ready for trouble, MacPherson, we've got company." But as he looked down at the cop car expecting to lock eyes with Rothwell or Jenkins, he saw that the driver was wearing a baseball cap from which flowed tresses of golden hair.

"Charlie!" he said in total disbelief, and as his eyes met hers he was rewarded with a smile he would never forget.

From his left MacPherson spoke: "My daughter is a very resourceful girl and also one who doesn't like to be kept in the dark, Mr Fear. I'm afraid she gave me no option but to include her in the planning of this Heist, and it has proved a very good move…wouldn't you agree?"

"Bleedin' hell, Obadiah, I didn't see that one comin', cuz! Sweet little Charlie…who would have thought," exclaimed Johnny The Shark, who was clearly as shocked as Fear.

Trying to take all of it in and also keep his attention on the M8, Fear shook his head ruefully. He returned his gaze to Charlie, who gave him a quick wave before dropping the Focus back behind the ambulance.

"I think you owe me an explanation, MacPherson," he demanded.

The Cyclops smiled disingenuously: "All in good time, after we've switched cars. But it's safe to say that DS Ricky Jenkins is no longer a threat to us and that we have DI Rothwell by the proverbials…he just doesn't know it. Once we are at the safe house for the switch you will text him with his next instructions, and then we will take care of Rothwell once and for all, and – just hopefully – we will have taken care of our final loose end. Then I'll put you in the picture… you've earned that and it's the least I can do."

"So where we headed?" asked Fear.

"The back roads between Milngavie and Stirling offer a myriad of boltholes, twisting dirt tracks and ramshackle farmhouses, and it's at one of these that we will switch things around, destroy the ambulance and our clothing and anything else that could connect us to the airport job and the £40 million we've just bagged."

"What about the Fire Tender?"

"Sadly Marty will be ensuring the demise of that magnificent vehicle in a similar scene of destruction at a similar destination somewhere between here and the good City of

Stirling. Now, if you don't mind, take the slip road for the Clyde Tunnel, and then follow the signs for Milngavie. So far so good!" said MacPherson, moulding himself into the ambulance cabin seat and folding his arms in satisfaction.

As Fear indicated to take the approaching slip road for the Clyde Tunnel he checked his mirror for the reassuring form of Charlie in the Ford Focus. But as his eyes homed in on her vehicle he was suddenly distracted by the flashing lights and sleek lines of a BMW 530 in full marked livery surging down the overtake lane 200 yards behind her.

52

"SHIT," Fear said: "This time we really do have trouble… jam sandwich firing down the outside lane…fingers crossed he ain't comin' our way and that Charlie has seen him."

The mobile was already at MacPherson's lips: "Have you picked up the cop car 100 yards behind you?"

Fear could just hear Charlie's voice reply: "Yep."

"We need you to buy as much time as you can before we hit the Clyde Tunnel…good luck, my darling girl," MacPherson said calmly, but Fear could see the tension in his face.

"Okay, let's get a move on. There's no point hanging about. If Smokey is coming our way we've got to hit the Clyde Tunnel before he catches his bandit, otherwise this is going to turn very nasty."

"Understood," Fear said, moving through the gears and putting his foot down.

The ambulance shot down the slip road and then joined the main arterial route from the south side of the Clyde Tunnel. Fear checked the mirror again, but it was too late to see how Charlie was doing. He quickly murmured a silent prayer to the man above that Charlie would be okay.

****

As the marked Police Scotland BMW sped along the overtake lane Charlie waited for it to head left towards the slip road, a move that would be the final confirmation that the ambulance was its target.

As she guided the Focus onto the slip lane, she banged on her brakes, causing the VW behind her to almost smash into her rear bumper. Checking her rear mirror she saw the driver, a middle-aged man, ranting and pointing to her head implying she was crazy.

But the manoeuvre had caused a domino effect, shunting all of the traffic on the slip road up together, and for a moment the police car's progress was slowed amid a melee of flashing lights and angry horns.

Although Charlie could see the ambulance approach the final bend and begin the descent into the tunnel, her job was only partially done, as the main route into the underpass was a dual carriageway. Once the traffic vehicle was on it, it would be almost impossible to halt its progress any further without making it obvious what she was up to and potentially compromising the whole operation.

With the junction of the slip road and the dual carriageway fast approaching she saw that the line of vehicles behind her had started to zigzag left and right, to allow the police vehicle safe passage.

It was then that she played her trump card.

Her baseball cap long since discarded, Charlie's blonde hair cascaded down over her shoulders, and just as she reached the junction, she started to straddle both lanes and stalled the Focus.

The eruption of horns from behind provided concrete proof of the chaos she had caused, and throwing her hands up in the air, she mimed exasperation at her apparent misfortune.

As she did so Charlie saw that 800 yards in front of her the ambulance was nowhere to be seen, and smiling she pretended to repeatedly turn her ignition key in a vain effort to get the vehicle to start.

Then suddenly the Focus was jolted to the left by a dunt from the marked police vehicle, which now proceeded to shove the Ford from the middle of the slip lane and force its way by. As she looked up, the cop sitting in the passenger seat slid his window down and raged: "You've chosen a helluva time to have a blonde moment, lady! The Airport's been robbed and two guards killed. Move!"

Charlie smiled her apology sweetly and mouthed a: "Sorry," but the cop car was already surging past and snaking down the dual carriageway. She reached for her phone and waited for her father to pick up: "The police car is past me, and it's coming down the dual carriageway. They're armed and are responding to the Airport robbery," she said breathlessly.

"Thank you! You okay?" asked MacPherson.

"Nope, just another dumb blonde, stalling her car in heavy traffic!"

"Okay, get yourself back to Lanarkyngs and wait for me…if we don't make it back you know what to do," MacPherson said.

"Take care, dad," replied Charlie but the line had already gone dead.

****

As the ambulance entered the tunnel its progress was impeded by a Hutcheson's Academy minibus full of teenagers that was trundling down the initial dip in the southbound carriageway. Its driver, a teacher taking a load of teenage rugby players to an inter-schools tournament, blissfully unaware of the ambulance that was now just yards behind him.

But with traffic two-way in the tunnel the ambulance's progress was slowed down dramatically and across the other side of the cabin MacPherson could see Fear nervously checking his mirror.

Just as Fear mouthed the question, Johnny The Shark beat him to it: "What's Charlie saying, cuz?"

"Armed Response Vehicle is responding to the airport robbery, one of the cops let slip to Charlie on the way past. They know that two guards are down...they didn't mention anything about an ambulance but..."

Before The Cyclops could finish his sentence he was interrupted by the wail of a siren and as he checked his mirror for the umpteenth time, Fear could see that the Police Vehicle had entered the tunnel.

"Fuck it, here they come."

53

"Got them in my mirror," said Johnny, flicking a worried glance MacPherson's way.

"Let's just play it cool until we know for sure they are after us," advised MacPherson.

"Aah come on, cuz, why else are they gonna be in the bleedin' tunnel?" We already know they're responding to the airport job…" said Johnny.

But as Fear monitored his driver's mirror he could see that any doubt about the identity of the police vehicle's quarry was now gone: it had surged out of the south lane and started to force oncoming traffic to grind to a stop.

"Okay, there ain't no point in having a flashing light on the roof and a siren if we can't use it when the shit hits the fan…buckle up, boys…here we go," he exclaimed.

Lights flashing and siren howling, Fear snapped the ambulance out from behind the minibus and onto the northbound lane as the tunnel started to dip. About 100 yards in front of him an oncoming bus was headed their way. He gritted his teeth and flattened the accelerator, swerving the ambulance back into the south lane with ten yards to spare, as the shocked driver slapped his forehead with the palm of his hand and flicked him a derisory finger.

"Bloody bus drivers don't give a shit about anyone else on the road! If they don't bother moving for an ambulance I'm bettin' they'll show the cops just about as much respect as they did for us!" In the mirror he could see the cop car had indeed had its path blocked by the bus and been forced to pull back in behind the school mini-bus.

Seizing his advantage Fear once again accelerated out into the northbound lane and made the most of a quiet stretch to draw away from their pursuers, only for the ambulance's progress to be blocked by a smart car with two female occupants who appeared so deep in conversation that they were oblivious to the emergency vehicle's pyrotechnics.

This time Fear just managed to swerve the ambulance in behind a blue Volvo 4x4 and as he did so MacPherson gave him the good news: "Cop car is back on our tail and closing."

The ambulance was no match for the turbo-charged BMW of the Police Scotland ARV, and as the smart car drove past Fear could see the cop vehicle, just yards behind him, suddenly pull almost adjacent on the now empty northbound carriageway.

It was then that the police car's loudspeakers barked into action: "This is Police Scotland. Driver of the ambulance: pull into the side and stop immediately!"

"Fuck you," spat Fear, and just as the ARV drew level with the ambulance he flashed a wicked smile and ripped the steering wheel hard to his right, smashing into his pursuer, ramming the ARV into the tunnel's north wall and sending a thousand sparks flying into the air.

From the back of the ambulance Williams shouted: "For fuck's sake, will ye get tae...bastard coppers!"

The manoeuvre had given the ambulance a reprieve, and Fear shot temporarily clear. He could see the ARV driver righting his vehicle before it resumed tailgating, and once again the loudspeaker sprang to life: "This is your final warning. You are being pursued by armed police. Pull into the side and stop your vehicle."

Johnny had had enough. He slid his window down and pulled a Glock from inside his green ambulance fatigues, adopting a firing position that had him hanging half out the window.

"Fuckin' cops…time you had some breakfast. Eat this!" The sharp report of the Gen4 Glock 17 echoed out in the tunnel as he unloaded three 9x19mm Parabellum cartridges in the direction of the ARV.

The police vehicle swerved violently in its attempt to avoid Johnny's salvo, but one of the shots smashed the windscreen plumb centre in the space between the two cops manning it.

The driver smashed out the window with a gloved fist as his colleague took aim with his Heckler & Koch carbine and returned lead with interest.

"For fuck's sake…that worked a bloody treat…you've disturbed a hornets' nest…just get back in the cabin…now!" ordered Fear.

MacPherson attempted to mollify his driver's wrath: "The die is cast, Fear. I brought you in on this job for precisely this type of moment…now would be a good time to produce the goods…" But before MacPherson could finish, Fear's mirror smashed as the cops sent their best wishes.

Fear slid the ambulance back into the northbound lane, but this time the cop car surprised him by shooting into the space he had vacated in the south channel.

"Fuck it, I ain't havin' this anymore," spat Johnny, and once again levelled his Glock out the passenger window.

"For Chrissakes, make it count and take out a tyre if you can, Johnny!" shouted The Cyclops; but before Johnny could even get a shot away the cop car rammed hard into the ambulance's offside and now it was Fear who found his vehicle jammed up against the north wall of the tunnel amidst a hail of sparks and the agonising rasping screeching metal.

He jerked the steering well hard to the left but could not budge the ARV. Yet that was the least of his troubles...with the two vehicles wedged together and now occupying both sides of the tunnel, he saw the massive shape of a council dump truck cresting the brow of the North lane and starting its descent.

The driver reaching onto his dashboard, grabbed a sandwich, which he started to devour with manic greed.

MacPherson had seen the looming danger as well: "Come on, Fear..." he snapped, pushing against the ambulance dashboard with so much pressure his hands turned white.

"Fuck's sake, he's sighting me up in the H&K, Fear, you gotta do somefin..." screamed Johnny.

Ramming on the brakes with all his might, Fear brought the ambulance to a shuddering halt that forced the ARV to disengage from it. As the police vehicle sprang free it's driver lost control of the steering wheel, and the three of them watched wide-eyed as the cop car started to rotate onto its side and somersaulted towards the advancing dump truck, which continued directly towards it.

In the council vehicle's cabin Fear saw that the sandwich had now fallen out of the driver's mouth as he frantically attempted to bring the 20-ton vehicle to a stop.

It was an exercise in futility, and on its third somersault the ARV cannoned up off the tarmacadam of the road surface and smashed into the front of the waste disposal truck.

Seeing the south lane of the tunnel clear, Fear quickly changed up through the ambulance gears and accelerated for all he was worth, but as the emergency vehicle shot up the incline the air was filled with the deafening thunder of an almighty explosion from the ARV'S spectacular impact with the dump truck, and a huge ball of flame filled the tunnel.

"Windows up, heads fuckin' down," ordered Fear with a grimace, holding onto the ambulance steering wheel for all he was worth and crouching down behind it.

MacPherson stared straight ahead but from the other side of the cabin Fear could hear praying: "Hail Mary, full of grace, the Lord is with thee. Blessed art thou among women, and blessed is the fruit of thy womb, Jesus. Holy Mary, mother of God, pray for us sinners, now and at the hour of our death. Amen!" wailed Johnny The Shark, curling into a ball.

54

THE ambulance hit the wall of flame at 70mph just as the bonnet of the ARV exploded through the air, smashing against the side of the emergency vehicle.

Holding the steering wheel with all his might, Fear managed to keep the ambulance steady and absorb the blow's impact. He snuck a quick glimpse and saw that the cop car's interior was now filled with flames. One of the dump truck crew had turned into a two-legged inferno and jumped from the cabin, screaming like a demented banshee.

It was the stuff of nightmares, and Johnny The Shark crossed himself repeatedly. It was clear that there would be no survivors from this lethal impact.

Blasting through the flame, the ambulance broke clear onto the empty southbound carriageway. As they emerged into daylight, Fear took the left filter lane for Whiteinch.

"What the fuck do you think you're doing?" demanded The Cyclops, aware that he had deviated from their designated escape route.

"We need to get rid of the ambulance as quickly as poss' before the cops have their bird flying. Every patrol car in Glasgow will be after us. We need somewhere with a ready source of vehicles, where we can dump the ambulance, get it torched and get rid of the Green Cross Code Man suits that will make us sitting ducks. I know a backstreet garage in Whiteinch less than a mile away where we can get off the grid and take care of all of that, no questions asked, then get the hell out of Glasgow with the cops still looking for an ambulance and three green men."

"Good shout, Fear. I should have thought of that," admitted MacPherson, clearly shaken by the proceeding moments.

It was the first time that Fear had heard The Cyclops admit fallibility.

"Blow me, I thought we was fucked back there. So what now, El Agente Grant?" asked Johnny The Shark, uncurled from his ball.

As Fear slid the ambulance off Dumbarton Road and onto a back street, less than half a mile from the Clyde Tunnel, he smiled for what seemed like the first time that day: "You sit in the cabin and leave the rest to me."

The ambulance came to a bumpy halt on cobblestones in front of a set of three black arched wooden doors, the middle one of which was open, while from within a bright light was shining out as The Chris Evans Breakfast Show blared from a radio.

Above the arches there was a sign proclaiming 'The Anchor Garage' and to reinforce the point a giant black Anchor hung from the brickwork just above the middle arch.

Slamming the driver's door behind him Fear walked towards the light, as Johnny and MacPherson eyed each other uncertainly. But before he reached the archway a man with a thatch of black hair and an ample beard strode out.

"Ludovic-fuckin'-Fear, as I live and breathe!" he exclaimed.

"Blackie, son. How are you mate? Business must be good if you're already on the job before 0700hrs!" replied Fear as they clasped hands in an act of old comradeship remembered and rejoined.

"Why're you here again, my old friend?" asked Blackie, pointing towards the badly dented ambulance and adding: "The Ambulance Service...I knew things had gone tits up for you but...surely you could have managed something better than that?" and at that Blackie gave Fear's green boiler suit a playful tug. He pointed towards the warmth coming from the garage entrance.

With time of the essence Fear's voice quivered with urgency: "I haven't got the time to paint you the whole picture, Blackie mate, but I'm deep in the shit, and I need you to make the ambulance disappear and provide us with a new motor, preferably a van. Some new kit wouldn't go amiss and I need it to happen...well...now," concluded Fear, trying to get a read on his old comrade's saturnine features.

"This wouldn't have anything to do with the Glasgow Airport Heist that's been all over the news since I opened up an hour ago?"

Fear shook his head grimly: "It does but...can you help an old mate out, Blackie? 'cause if I swing for this they'll throw away the key."

Blackie's brooding dark eyes pierced Fear for a moment of interminable torture and then he spoke: "You saved my bacon in Sangin, so if I can't return the favour what would that make me? I'm gonna open up the left arch. Get the ambulance driven in there as quick as your sorry arse can, and tell your boys to come straight in through the middle arch and we'll see what we can do, Ludo." But as Fear started to make his way towards the ambulance Blackie's gravelly voice spoke again: "Two guards dead, a cop car blown to smithereens, the Clyde Tunnel closed...what the fuck have you got yourself mixed up in, Ludo?" he asked.

Fear half-turned: "Like I say, if I get out of this in one piece I'll buy you a pint and give you the whole soddin' story."

Moments later he climbed back into the ambulance cabin: "Blackie's an old friend of mine from The Regiment, he's going to sort us out okay. MacPherson, if you follow him into the garage he will get things going. Johnny, I'm gonna need you to help me and Williams get the dough out of the ambulance before it's disposed of."

As Fear drove the ambulance into the left-hand arch MacPherson snapped: "Are you 100 per cent we can trust this…Blackie?"

Fear's reply was an icy glare. He pulled on the handbrake, bringing the vehicle to a stop above a mechanic's pit: "Look, MacPherson, he's all we've got. Your disposal of the two security guards, never mind the fireball that consumed the two cops and the dump truck crew back in the tunnel, has just made us the most wanted men in the UK. As for Blackie, I trust him with my life. So why don't you get in there, see what he's got for us and treat him with a bit of respect. We'll bring the bags of cash through pronto."

They worked with manic energy, and within 15 minutes the ambulance had been cleared of its lucrative cargo, which was now standing stacked just behind Blackie's office window.

He led them into the dirty little room. Five chipped enamel mugs and a packet of half-covered McVities digestives sat on an upturned crate as Blackie tuned into Radio 2 for the 7.30 am news.

Moira Stewart's sultry tones confirmed their worst fears. With a trail of two shot security guards and now the latest update revealing that two cops and the disposal truck crew had been killed in the car crash, they were the most wanted men in Britain.

Taking a final mouthful of over-stewed tea, Blackie gave his own bulletin: "Okay, I've got a black Transit Van that my boy uses to hump his mixer decks about, it'll be perfect for you. As for your Green Cross Code outfits, throw them in that metal drum, and I'll burn them. I have a set of mechanics' boiler suits here that maybe won't be a perfect fit, but will do until you reach the safe house I presume you've lined up. In ten minutes you can be gone from here, and no one will be any the wiser."

"What about the ambulance?" asked MacPherson.

"You leave that to me pal – but within the hour it will have vanished without a trace. Now...if you've finished your tea...I suggest you do the same."

MacPherson smiled and nodded his head in agreement. He reached over and grabbed one of the holdalls, unzipped it and fished out a wad of £100 notes.

Flicking through them he made a quick count "There must be £50k there...Blackie...if I may call you that? Please take this as a token of our appreciation for your help this morning." Then he leant forward and placed the bundle of notes down next to Blackie's mug, which proudly bore the crest of the St Mirren football club.

"Aye, maybees ye can use the readies tae buy yer team!" quipped Williams pointing at the chipped black and white drinking vessel, and for just a moment the tension dissolved.

55

As the black Ford Transit snaked along the minor roads leading back into Stirlingshire, Fear's mind started to refocus on Charlie's cameo role as the driver of the crash car.

Their journey out of Glasgow had been made largely in silence and all the while he had been working on the fact that she had clearly been in on 'The Heist', or 'the project', as MacPherson had referred to it from day one. It was also apparent that Charlie had the type of hidden resourcefulness that had allowed her to dispose of Jenkins…and he had to conclude that he'd been played.

With Johnny in the back minding the cash alongside Williams, the opportunity to speak freely had finally arrived.

"So MacPherson, when were you gonna tell me that Charlie was in on the whole op from day one? Would you stoop so low you'd use your own daughter as a honey trap, a sweetener to keep me happy? All that stuff about you being a father just like me…Christ, how can you look at yourself in the mirror, man?"

MacPherson turned his lopsided glance Fear's way: "I'm afraid you are only partially right, Mr Fear. Yes, my darling daughter is a very resourceful young lady, and yes, she has been involved from the get-go…because one day I hope to pass on the proceedings of this morning's work to her, so she can enjoy the life she deserves – at Lanarkyngs."

From the other side of the cabin Fear snorted derisorily: "Really?"

"But as to the honey trap aspect of it, you are well wide of the mark. Charlie's – how shall I describe it – involvement with you is the last thing I either wanted or needed. Quite frankly it's a complication I could well have done without. But that's going to be something for you and her to sort out. What's of more importance right now is what we are going to do with a certain DCI Rothwell…wouldn't you agree?"

"Charlie has been keeping him sweet masquerading as Jenkins via text message?"

"Naturally! But we both know that process will come to an end very quickly with the news of our little jolly being trumpeted to the heavens. We need you to send Rothwell an update that will get him to a place of our choosing, alone and ready to be put out his misery once and for all. Then, just maybe, with the last loose end tied up, we can look forward to enjoying our ill-gotten gains," concluded The Cyclops, a slight smile flickering over his face.

"Come on, MacPherson – we take care of one more bent cop and you think its happy days are here again? How are we ever gonna get away with this? Even if that security guard doesn't put two and two together and work out who the ambulance driver he thought he recognised was, someone down the chain will blab…they always do."

"The guard can always be made to go away on permanent vacation. Of course there can be no guarantees…but I find that terror is a good way to keep people quiet. Although perhaps in your case it is the promise of having some sort of a future that may work best. But what matters now is that you call Rothwell and get him where we want him, when we want him there."

"And tell me just how're we going to do that? The penny will have dropped that it was us behind the airport job so the horse has bolted in that respect…unless…" But before Fear could complete his hypothesis MacPherson did it for him.

"For Rothwell it's all about the promise of busting us with the loot, preferably while we're all still present and dividing our filthy lucre up. About a mile away on the right is a small turning that will take us to our original meeting point. There is an old cottage there where Marty will be waiting with everything we need to complete the home leg. Once we've concluded the minutiae I suggest you make the call. Rothwell has made things all too personal between me and him by taking out a very old friend of mine…it's time he paid for that misdemeanour with his eternal silence."

The Transit made its way through the Oakwood via a broken one-track road and after a quarter of a mile of painful jolts and bumps the whitewashed walls of a small cottage came into view, its billowing chimney making clear that Vallance and his crew were already in residence.

But as the Transit drew to a stop Fear's mobile went off. Fishing it out his overall pocket he squinted at the number a second time: "Shit. It's Rothwell!"

MacPherson's eyebrow raised in surprise: "You're going to have to play for time. We need to get a feel for what he's got planned; but if he pushes you then tell him you'll meet him at 4 pm today. We need time to get this all sorted."

Fear flicked his mobile to receive the call and was met with Rothwell's blunt tones: "Well, well, Fear, I'm surprised you've actually taken my call. It's been abundantly apparent that you were never going to bell me."

"That's not the case, Rothwell. I think you know why that is…don't you? I'd have thought it obvious that I've never had a chance to get time on my own to make the call...until right now...but you've beaten me to it. I've got news for you alright..."

But before he could complete Rothwell butted in: "Your news is old news and it's plastered over every available media outlet in Scotland and trending all over social media in the UK right now. But never mind that Fear...I've got someone here who wants to speak to you."

There was silence at Rothwell's end of the mobile, and then a child's voice spoke: "Daddy, daddy please, please come and get me...I'm scared."

56

THIS time the silence came from Fear's end of the mobile, his shock total and utter.

"Monty...are you okay? Where are you?" he asked, flicking on the mobile's speaker facility.

"I'm...stop it, leave me alone..." was as far as his son got and then the mobile was wrestled from him amid the sounds of a scuffle that was followed by the sound of Monty crying.

Then Rothwell was back on the other end: "Never mind where your little boy is. All you need to know, Fear, is that he is safe...for now. Whether young Monty remains that way depends on you."

"Listen to me, Rothwell, so help me God, you so much as harm a hair on his head and you're a dead man," spat Fear.

"You mean a dead man like DS Jenkins? Do you think I'm a fool? I don't know how she's done it, but the MacPherson bitch has clearly managed to escape his tender care and that can mean only one thing: you and the MacPhersons are as...as thick as thieves!"

Fear tried desperately to stall as MacPherson pointed to his watch and held up four fingers from the other side of the cabin, while outside the vehicle he could see Charlie was walking towards the ambulance.

"I don't know what the hell you're on about, Rothwell. But if anything happens to my boy you'll be eyes on for the rest of your days, never be able to stop looking over your shoulder until I take you down...then you'll wish you were dead already."

"What do you think this is, Fear – a scene from Ultimate-fuckin'-Force? Or was that for your audience? I'll bet you've put me on speaker and your new buddy The Cyclops is sitting listening to every word with his dear daughter Charlie holding your hand? Did she tell you how she disposed of DS Jenkins? Christ, the flat was an absolute bloodbath, poor bastard...I'd watch yourself with that one, Fear...you'll be the one needing to sleep with one eye open..."

But a combination of Fear's anger and impatience burst their banks: "Look, I'm here, alone in the middle of nowhere talking to you Rothwell, so cut the amateur dramatics...tell me exactly what it is you want me to do?"

"You won't need to worry about little Monty...as long as you do exactly what I say...but this is your last chance. Fuck up and..." Rothwell let his words trail off ominously.

"It's now 0915hrs. I will give you one hour to meet me and then accompany me on a Voluntary Attendance to Randolphfield Police Station, where you will turn Queen's evidence and give me everything on this morning's Heist. Plucky little Monty will then be returned to his mother unharmed, you escape from the grasp of The Cyclops and earn a shot at a new future in splendid anonymity where none of the ghosts of Christmas Past can haunt you, like supposedly de-commissioned IRA Active Service Units, can track you down. I get the collar of the century and all the players in the biggest armed robbery in British criminal history served to me on a plate and the loot as well. That way we both get what we want. It's simple really!" Then Rothwell's harsh laughter boomed out.

A foot away from him MacPherson was scribbling furiously on a notepad before holding it up for Fear to read: 'Agree. Play for time, 1hr not enough'.

Outside the passenger window Charlie's sculpted features had materialised but her smile of greeting was changing to a worried frown as she began to realise all was far from well.

"Look, Rothwell, there's no way I can be anywhere in an hour from Timbuck-fuckin'-tu. Can we make it 1100hrs? Will you have Monty with you?"

"Come on, Fear…do you think I came up the Clyde in a bleeding banana skin? No, my friend, your son will be released when we arrive at the front door of Randolphfield Police Station…you'll just have to trust me on that…in any case, you have no choice. Okay, I'll give you until 1030hrs… make sure you are in Café Nero at the foot of King Street in Stirling bang on the time. If not you will never see your son alive again," and at that the mobile went dead. Fear held his phone inches in front of him, staring at it in incomprehension.

The passenger door opened from the other side of the cabin and Charlie asked: "What's wrong?"

"Rothwell has taken his son," said MacPherson, turning towards Fear.

But he had already bolted out of the driver's door and made for a giant oak tree that dominated the field just to the left of the steading. He paced beneath it, furiously running his hands through his hair. MacPherson and his daughter followed in his wake.

"Maybe it doesn't seem it, but there is a way out of this. There's no way Rothwell has abducted the boy in an official capacity. So we know he's acting rogue. The key is finding out where he's holding Monty and wresting your boy from whoever is holding him before you're forced to step inside the cop shop."

Fear had sat down with his back against the base of the mighty oak, his right hand still filleting his sandy mop as

Charlie knelt down beside him. "What if he doesn't have anyone else to keep Monty captive? I mean, how many bent cops can there be? If that were the case then as long as we can locate Monty before you get to Randolphfield and confirm he is safe, then whatever happens to the Detective Chief Inspector will be up to you, Ludovic, my friend," MacPherson continued.

The smile MacPherson gave him seemed genuine, and Fear felt his hope reviving.

"So we split. I meet Rothwell and you find Monty? But what about all of this?" he asked, pointing at the frantic activity that was going on around the cottage where Vallance's powerful figure could now be seen outside the front door, hands on hips, a puzzled look etched on his brooding features.

"Marty will take care of it all, get everything back to Lanarkyngs and make sure there is no trail left in the process. Now, we know you're meeting Rothwell at Café Nero. How do we work out where he's going to be holding Monty?"

"How many safe houses can he have? He's obviously been back to the flat, 'cos he's seen Jenkins' body. Every new location that gets used increases his own chance of being detected and caught going rogue, as you called it," concluded Fear, his senses returning quickly.

"So you think your son could be in that same flat, gagged and bound while he looks to hook you?"

"It's all we've got. You've got to find and free Monty. Text me, because without that info I'm powerless to take down Rothwell."

"And how will you do that?" asked The Cyclops.

"You'll know soon enough. But first you need to find my son and let me know he is safe…Christ, what've I done?" Fear whispered, his voice faltering with raw emotion.

57

FEAR strode through the glass doors of Café Nero, checking the wall clock as he entered and breathing a sigh of relief when it confirmed he was five minutes early.

He scanned the comfortable leather couches and the smiling faces of punters enjoying their Mochas and Lattes, but no Rothwell. He felt his heart hammering.

Fear forced himself to take a deep breath. Rothwell had to be here because he needed him: 'Without me you've nothing, you bastard,' chimed his inner voice.

Walking past the queue of caffeine-addicts lining the service counter, Fear reached the end of the room, turned the corner and saw a set of wooden steps leading to a first floor. He took them two at a time.

Sitting on a leather armchair facing the stairway was Rothwell, his hands steepled, his florid face lit with a broadening sickly smile. Fear closed the ten-foot gap between them in three strides and dropped into the empty chair opposite.

"Mr Fear, how nice of you to join me, " said Rothwell and checked his Patek Philipe: "And with a couple of minutes to spare. But if your son's life being on the line can't inject some urgency into you, then what will?"

Through gritted teeth Fear snapped: "Get Monty on the other end of the mobile…now!"

"I'm sorry, but that isn't possible. All you need to do is play ball. We'll walk in the door at Randolphfield and the minute you sign the VA he'll be free to return to mummy, safe, sound and no real harm done."

The fact that Rothwell refused to get Monty on the phone was the confirmation Fear needed that, with Jenkins dead, the DI had run out of sidekicks.

His son was bound and gagged but also almost certainly alone: "Please God let him be in the flat," muttered Fear despite himself.

"What was that?" asked Rothwell curiously.

"I said you better not be fuckin' with me, you twat. Now can we get this done?" The rustling of a *London Times* saw a bespectacled elderly gent enfilade Fear with a disgusted look.

Fear ignored him, but it underlined why Rothwell had chosen the coffee shop as their meeting place: with so many witnesses, he felt safe.

The DCI smiled as if he knew exactly what Fear was thinking: "There's no rush. I took the liberty of ordering you a coffee, but we can finish en route if need be…aah here we are," beamed Rothwell as a dark-haired, lively eyed waitress arrived.

"Latte to go for you sir?" she asked in a pleasing Irish burr, and Fear nodded in the affirmative and smiled back as she walked away.

"A pleasing young filly!" smiled Rothwell: "Plenty of time for that once we've concluded our business. But before we go anywhere we need to establish a few ground rules that will stop you doing anything stupid that might – how shall I say – compromise your son's safety."

"Look, I'll give you everything you want as long as Monty is okay and I have guarantees in place from someone far higher up the tree than you, Rothwell, that in turning Queen's evidence I can start afresh with no backdraft coming my way."

"You have no fears on that account, I can assure you," said Rothwell bursting into a chesty cough.

As he did, the sound of a bottle being opened confirmed Fear had a text.

Praying that it would be the information he craved, Fear checked his cell phone: 'Monty good all well!' Inside, Fear breathed a huge sigh of relief and said a mental 'thank you' to the big man upstairs.

Rothwell's eyes quickly settled on Fear's mobile, but, his coughing fit showing no sign of subsiding, he got to his feet: "I need some water," he grunted and quickly headed for the toilet to his right.

As he made his way through the door Fear took a quick glance in the direction of the tutting elderly man and seeing, his *Times* was still held up, fished out a small vial, containing a few grams of a yellowish powder.

For a moment he looked at the pod, aware that what he was about to do next would ultimately decide his own fate, never mind Rothwell's.

'How can you trust a bastard like Rothwell? Man, he'd betray his own granny for a leg up,' snapped the voice in his head, and a slight smile twitched at the corners of his mouth.

Fear knew his path was chosen.

He slipped the ampule open with the reverse end of his spoon, deftly unscrewed the lid from the coffee carton and emptied the capsule's contents into Rothwell's Americano. He gave it a stir and replaced the cap, before sitting back in his chair.

Within a couple of minutes Rothwell returned. He drew to a halt a foot away from the coffee table and said: "Time we hit the road, Fear. The moment of truth has finally arrived."

Fear clutched his Latte container in one hand and lifted Rothwell's with his other, handing it to him with an amicable smile: "You might as well take it…just in case you've another coughing fit?"

"Such consideration," replied Rothwell, but before he took the cup he dropped a set of car keys on the table and Fear could see that his left hand, which was inside his jacket pocket, was angling something sinister his way.

"You'll be driving, Fear, and if you try anything smart I won't hesitate to use this," he said, drawing the handle of his handgun slightly out of the pocket.

As Rothwell took the coffee container, Fear leant down and lifted the keys: "Look, I'm not gonna be doing anything to screw things up now, I just want to get it done and see my son again."

"You first. When we get out the front door turn left up King Street, and you'll see a grey Mondeo parked 100 yards up. That's our car. I'll be one step behind you all the way."

****

Rothwell took a sip from his card coffee cup as Fear walked warily towards the vehicle. Moments later the DI sat with what he now identified was the distinctive green polymer frame of a semi-automatic Walther P99, pointing at him from the passenger seat. In silence he engaged first and manoeuvred the vehicle out of its parking bay and up the cobbles of King Street.

Looking up he saw the imposing statue of Sir William Wallace perched on top of a classically triple-arched portico, staring down from the front of The Athenaeum, a magnificent oval-shaped building originally created as a reading room in 1816. Fear wondered if Wallace's glower was disapproving.

"Quite a sight, old Wallace!" he said conversationally, but he was pleased to see that Rothwell was too busy guzzling his Americano to be able to reply.

"Don't know what it is, but I could swear Nero's coffee tastes better from cardboard than coffee cup! So, Fear, what are you going to do when this is all done and you can start afresh?" asked the DCI, who then gave his head an inadvertent shake.

"I dunno, cross that bridge when I come to it, I guess," answered Fear, watching his passenger out of the corner of his eye, like a hawk.

Again Rothwell's head started to dip and his eyelids drooped as if they weighed a ton.

"Not quite yourself?" Fear asked blandly.

But there was no reply from the passenger seat as Rothwell slumped into unconsciousness.

Smiling, Fear reached over and slipped the Walther from his captor's grip. The high dosage of GHB, otherwise known as liquid ecstasy, had done its trick.

"Time you got what's coming to you, my friend," he said and slid the Mondeo left onto the Dumbarton Road, heading for Lanarkyngs.

58

FEAR drew to a halt just as the glade swallowed the end of the track as if it had never existed.

Rothwell was still out cold. Exiting from the driver's side he made his way around the vehicle and opened the passenger door, looking down at the comatose policeman.

From behind Fear the snap of a twig served notice he had company: "So, you made it out with our friend, no problem?" asked The Cyclops.

Turning, he saw that MacPherson, his face set grim, was flanked by both Vallance and Johnny The Shark, and for a moment he wondered just what this intimidating welcoming committee had planned.

"If you get the good DCI out, Marty, Johnny and I can take care of him from here. I have a particularly poetic form of justice awaiting our over-ambitious friend – and one that'll serve him well for the demise of a good friend."

But then MacPherson realised that Fear's was looking beyond and above him, to the towering stone edifice that dominated the surrounding woodland.

"Ah, yes: I see you're quite taken with the MacPherson Monument. Let's walk while we talk and I'll tell you all about it," said The Cyclops, beckoning Fear to join him on the path that led to the glade.

"Where's Monty?" Fear demanded.

"Your boy is fine and being spoiled by his auntie Charlie in my office up at the Castle...where we'll meet them... once this is done," said MacPherson, clapping him on the shoulder as they drew parallel.

"This is the MacPherson Monument – quarried from blocks of red sandstone way back around 1800. You'll notice that the first 30 feet bear the shape of a tree trunk with branch stumps and scars to commemorate the history of my Clan. The lopped off branches and welds on the trunk of the tree signifying those members of the clan who perished during the imposition of the penal laws which were passed against us after Culloden, when we were proscribed and made outlaw. As you can see a three-column Roman Doric Rotunda grows out of the trunk and is topped, in turn, by a Roman Doric shaft on top of which once rested an intricately carved urn sporting the insignia of Clan MacPherson, the wildcat. Sadly, as you will also shortly observe, the urn now lies shattered and ruined like so much of Lanarkyngs, the immortal memory of my ancestors and the guardians of this dear green place betrayed by those that followed."

As they picked their way through the ferns, a groan from behind them suggested that Rothwell was starting to wake from his forced stupefaction.

Ten yards away the shattered urn duly appeared from the carpet of greenery underfoot: "They say that one way to measure a tree is to fall from it...it's a saying that has a particular resonance in this context here among the firs in this once sacred place...but now, it just fills me with melancholy," frowned MacPherson, a slight quiver detectable in his voice.

Again Fear found himself surprised by The Cyclops' sensitivity. MacPherson turned his disconcerting lopsided one eyed gaze his way: "Don't worry, Ludovic, one day soon it will all be restored to its former splendour...but first we must take care of our visitor."

Yards away Johnny and Vallance, each supporting one of Rothwell's arms, dragged his dead weight to the monument's base.

The DCI's eyelids, still clearly heavy, started to flicker.

"Strap him to the column," ordered MacPherson.

The effect of being slapped against cold sandstone and having his arms bound tight against the huge column brought Rothwell back to wide-eyed consciousness.

"What are you doing, you maniac? I'm a serving police officer! You'll never get away with this!"

"You may be a current serving police officer but you are one who has murdered a colleague and much more importantly an old friend of mine to help serve your own rotten ends..." replied MacPherson, letting his words taper off until the sound of Rothwell's heavy breathing and birdsong were all that filled the air.

"Let me do him, Obadiah," pleaded The Shark: "Why don't we have us a game of Russian Roulette?"

"What about you, Ludovic? What is the appropriate punishment to fit the good DCI's crimes?"

His jaw set firm, Fear said nothing but ripped the 9-milly from inside his Barbour and slammed the barrel against Rothwell's temple: "There's only one way to deal with treacherous scum like you, Rothwell. You're more rotten than any terrorist I ever killed and you know why? Because you're supposed to be the guardian of the innocent, serving your community, instead you've no morals, there is nothing you won't do to serve your own ends. It's you that the community needs protection from...you bastard!"

"How quaintly put!" said MacPherson: "But not the best use of a man, as – ah yes – as resourceful as DCI Rothwell here. Tempting though it maybe to execute our fallen law enforcer, I would ask you to remove your weapon from his head and consider this…" said The Cyclops, breaking into his squint-smile.

Fear stared back, his eyes pulsing with rage…for a moment he caressed the trigger.

"For pity's sake, Fear, you're a soldier, a man who has served Queen and Country with distinction, served the uniform just as I do. You know there is still a way out of this if you turn…"

But Fear finished the sentence for him: "Queen's evidence? We may both have worn the uniforms of our country but that is the only thing we have in common, Rothwell. You have embroiled women and children into your poisoned schemes and all for what? To further your own putrid purposes and now…now it must end."

Rothwell's eyes became saucers as he desperately pleaded for his life once more: "I'll give you anything you want, anything…just, please, just name your price."

As he stared death down the barrel, Fear's index finger began to pull the Browning's trigger back…

59

"No...please...I, I, I beg you...don't!" pleaded the DCI, but Fear tossed the Browning into a somersault and reclaimed it by the barrel: "Death would be too good for you!" he spat and pistol-whipped Rothwell hard and fast.

The remnants of a bloodied and broken tooth fell out of Rothwell's mouth as his head sagged.

Striding forward MacPherson grabbed the detective's chin between his index finger and his thumb and forced his gaze to meet his single eye: "You have gambled, Rothwell, and you have lost...but as I said you're too valuable to me to have terminated and...quite frankly, after the trouble and grief you've caused me that would be too easy. No, instead you will work for me and you will spend the rest of your days bearing my mark."

Then The Cyclops stepped back and snapped his fingers in Vallance's direction.

Before Fear had time to turn towards MacPherson's lieutenant, the look of sheer terror in Rothwell's eyes alerted him to what his fate would be.

"With pleasure, boss," spat Vallance and pulled out a Stanley knife.

"No, Marty, this pleasure will be all mine," replied MacPherson and held out his hand to claim the blade.

Reluctantly, Vallance handed it to The Cyclops, whose fist closed around it: "The motto of my clan is 'Touch not the cat bot a glove', DCI Rothwell. Bot means without, the glove of the wildcat on our clan crest is its pad. If the cat is ungloved, its claws are unsheathed."

Theatrically MacPherson flicked the blade high until its glinting edge stuck out from between his fingers: "The motto was meant to serve as a warning that one should beware when the wildcat's claws are without glove. It was a reference to the historically violent nature of Clan MacPherson and served as a metaphorical warning to the other clans that they should think twice before interfering with our business. You failed to do so, Rothwell, and now..." exulted MacPherson, his voice rising to a shout: "The cat is indeed bot a glove!" He strode forward to the cowering figure of Rothwell, who frantically strained at his bonds for all he was worth.

Rothwell screamed pitifully as The Cyclops' 'claw' began its descent; but there was to be no reprieve, and the blade inserted precisely just under Rothwell's right eye, before MacPherson proceeded to scoop out the orb as blood, mucus and gore spat from the hollowing eye socket.

As The Cyclops went about his bloodcurdling work the quiet of the forest was shattered by the DCI's endless, agonised screams echoing out like some warning from the depths of hell; but after what seemed like an eternity, standing back, MacPherson held his prize aloft: the bloodied eyeball and its trailing veins staring up from his outstretched palm.

From the pillar Rothwell gave one last pitiful sob and passed out.

"Cut him down," ordered MacPherson, tossing the blade to Vallance.

His bonds cut, Rothwell, hit the ground and started to regain consciousness. He desperately started fingering the bloody hollow where his right eye had been only moments before.

Looking up at MacPherson he whimpered: "You… you're insane MacPherson."

As he did so, The Cyclops extended his hand aloft as high as it would go: "Aah-ha…Lanarkyngs' crows are renowned for their intelligence Rothwell…" and as he looked up into the trees a flutter of wings could be heard, and the air was soon filled with a cawing as a dark shadow swooped down.

A huge black crow with a silvery streak running down its back hovered above MacPherson's hand for a moment, before jutting its beak forward and snapping the bloodied drooling eye from The Cyclops' palm.

On his knees Rothwell threw up.

Turning his head away from the sadism of The Cyclops' vengeance for McColl, Fear in turn swallowed down a mouthful of bile; he could see from Johnny The Shark's sheet-white features that he had not been the only one left in shock by the preceding moments.

"Get him up!" ordered MacPherson and as Vallance hauled the sobbing DCI to his feet and slammed him back against the monument, The Cyclops grabbed him by the throat once again.

"You're my creature now, Rothwell…forever you will bear my mark. In your avarice and vaulted, naked ambition you have created chains of your own making that mean you will have no voice, no credibility should you wish to throw any mud my way. Instead, your only hope is to serve me… unquestioningly."

One hand covering his empty, dripping eye socket, the other wiping the sputum from his mouth, Rothwell shivered uncontrollably as the shock of what had just been inflicted on him racked his body.

But The Cyclops had not finished: "Know this, what my friends and I have completed in the last 24 hours will allow me to go on building and extending my network beyond you and Police Scotland and into the Scottish government and other institutions equally full of venal, shallow individuals full of strutting self-importance. Wherever I see weakness I will find a way to exploit it and you, DCI Rothwell, will be my creature in this; serve me unstinting in that regard and by doing so you will prosper. And do you know why you will do so?"

Shaking uncontrollably as bloody slime slid down his cheek, Rothwell stared sullenly up with his remaining eye but said nothing.

"Because you have no choice!" and at that MacPherson grabbed the DCI's hand and thrust the Mondeo's car keys into his palm: "I suggest you take your vehicle and check-in at Forth Valley Royal. I will leave you to lick your wounds, but you will be watched and when the time comes…I will reach out from behind my veneer of respectability and legitimacy for you Rothwell…and you will be there for me. Now take your pitiful being from my soil…GO!" shouted MacPherson in sudden rage.

Stumbling past them, Rothwell staggered along the trodden grass pathway towards his vehicle, a broken wretch, as The Cyclops stared after him triumphantly.

"Sweet Christ," said Fear to himself.

60

MacPherson uncorked The 1974 and poured two glasses from the remainder of the bottle, pushed one across the table towards Fear, who remained standing.

Picking up a note, which Fear could see had been penned in Charlie's neat and precise handwriting, he quickly read out his daughter's words: "Took Monty up to the Chapel to show him the old graveyard and then the Bath House. All well, please come and get us when ready. C xxx."

Fear, some small part of him still suspecting a final act of treachery from the man who had exploited his capabilities so ruthlessly, breathed a little more freely.

"But before you go and get your boy we need to tie up our loose ends, don't you think? Prior to leaving Lanarkyngs you will receive an exceptionally generous payment for the work you've done for me…I don't want that work to end. You, my dear Ludovic, have exceeded my expectations. I now know that I can trust you beyond question. Indeed, had it not been for your skill behind the wheel back in The Clyde Tunnel, we would not be here right now toasting our success. Slàinte mhath! Mr Fear, you have surely earned it."

Wordlessly, Fear reciprocated.

His one eye peering over the top of the glass, MacPherson held Fear's gaze for a moment: "In a matter of hours Johnny will start to reinvest our bounty through a variety of business ventures that will provide no money trail; but these investments will ultimately bring me the finance I need to raise Lanarkyngs from its ashes and turn it into the foremost country hotel in Perthshire and the whole of the Lowlands," MacPherson said, then raised the whisky glass to his lips and sipped.

"You know that the poet A.E. Houseman once wrote of nostalgia: 'That is the land of lost content, I see it shining plain, the happy highways where I went and cannot come again.' But with this money I will reinvent my past and make it far better, brighter, bigger than it ever was in my childhood memories. Don't you sometimes wish you could do the same, Mr Fear?"

Feet away, Fear remained a study in still and silent life, once again surprised by The Cyclops' apparent need both to unburden and justify himself but also disconcerted by the question he'd left hanging in the air.

MacPherson hadn't finished: "Yet while my business may seem increasingly wholly legitimate…I will still have need of your services…but first I must know what your plans are?"

Fear drained the remains of the whisky and lightly placed the glass back on MacPherson's desk. He momentarily stared into the peat-laced flames.

Then taking a step back he smiled wistfully: "Beyond taking my son home, I dunno. You've already paid me well, and now I have the chance to start afresh somewhere else; but that would mean without Monty and I could not live with myself if I deserted him again…however lucrative the work is on The Circuit."

A light knock on the office door was followed by the cockney tones of Johnny The Shark: "Delivery for El Agente Grant," he laughed and dropped a black holdall at Fear's feet before extending his hand: "I gotta be on me way, matey, but before I go, I just wanted to say it's been a bleedin' blast. Sod me, but 'til the day I die I'll never forget that dodgem ride in the Glasgow Tunnel!"

"You mean the Clyde Tunnel, Johnny," said Fear, smiling and shaking his hand warmly.

"That's the bugga! Yeah, listen, matey, I hope we meets again but now," and Johnny turned to meet MacPherson's gaze: "I needs to be headin' back down the road and get the wheels in motion. You take care, Obadiah, and give sweet Charlie a peck from her uncle Johnny!"

A thin smile appeared on MacPherson's dark features: "God's speed, Johnny. Just make sure you keep me posted when you reach London, as agreed."

At that Johnny offered a mock salute and slid out the door.

Fear, despite himself, found he could not resist the urge to look down at the holdall and as he did so MacPherson spoke: "£1 million in used notes is the price of my gratitude and also, I hope, the retaining fee for your loyalty."

Fear hunkered down, unzipped the holdall and found the bag was indeed stuffed full of more bank notes than he'd ever seen before. Shaking his head he zipped it closed.

"I'm sorry, MacPherson, but I can't pocket any of that. Whatever way you look at it, there's the blood of innocent men on that money, I wouldn't feel right taking it," he said, retreating from the holdall.

For a moment MacPherson stared at him and then he sighed: "Come, come, Ludovic, it's a bit late in the day to be turning squeamish. Shirley made a botch of the one thing he had to do correctly, and as for his supervisor, there is no way we could have left him behind and not expected him to sing like a demented canary the first opportunity he got. Have you forgotten that he also did everything he could to help us set the alarm off? I think he was well paid in kind for his attempts to sabotage the project. As for the cops…collateral damage." MacPherson turned his palms upwards before continuing: "So, my friend, forget about them and think of yourself and your boy. That's the type of money that will make sure young Monty has the best start in life he can want, the type that eluded you and will help you in turn take away the guilt you clearly still feel at what has gone wrong with your family. With this type of money, you could wipe the slate clean, and I'm sure that would put a smile back on the lovely Gina's face. The contents of that bag are a game changer for you: they will allow you to set up in business any way you want, and as I said, you've earned it, Mr Fear. So why, in the words of the old song, don't you pack all your guilt away in your old kitbag and smile, smile, smile?"

Fear nodded his head grimly, but before he could reply MacPherson spoke again: "Look, this job has provided finance that will allow me to put plans in action that can bring a whole new world within reach, make anything possible; but like I said I'm going to have need of someone with your expertise who I can trust 100 per cent. I want you to come with me on that journey."

"I'm flattered, but I can't do it MacPherson. I don't have any problems taking out a scumbag, but this is different. As for Gina, well, I'm sorry to disappoint you but there's no way of patching things up there, and in any case, it's done. You've already paid me generously for my work, and that will help me make the new start I need. But now it's time I found my son."

MacPherson smiled wistfully: "It is indeed touching that you have such strong affections for your boy when your father clearly didn't entertain similar feelings for you."

The Cyclops' change of tack caught Fear cold and he couldn't stop a look of surprise enveloping his face: "Say what's on your mind, MacPherson."

"An appropriate location for this little tête-à-tête to take place...don't you think, in the shadow of the hero who, given the fact that you are an orphan, could almost be called your surrogate father?" recited MacPherson, repeating his own words.

"You'll remember the unfortunate business with Bancroft up at the statue of Sir David Stirling...but do you remember my words?"

Slowly signs of recollection slipped across Fear's stony countenance, but MacPherson held his hand up and continued: "I'm not the only bastard in this room, my dear Fear. Do you remember that I mentioned Sir David's close friend, the man who worked with him to create the SAS: Sir Archie McBride? Well, he was not merely your surrogate father through that work, he was the man who sired you!"

For a second time Fear's temper snapped and he sprang across the room and rammed The Cyclops against a damp wall, pinioning his neck back with a forearm and leaving MacPherson gagging for air: "I don't know what sick game you're playing, MacPherson, but you can forget it. The only parents I had were those who adopted me...end of. Clearly someone must have fathered me but Sir Archie McBride... utter garbage...he would have been in his sixties, for Chrissakes – and who was my natural mother then, the bloody Queen?" demanded Fear, a vein in his forehead throbbing.

MacPherson protested his innocence: "I'm playing no game with you; I had you researched extremely carefully... and there are some things we outside the law can find out when nobody else can. Also, this matters to me." He paused ruminatively. "As I know only too well, every man should have the chance to know from which tree he dropped. You, my friend, are the progenitor of one of the biggest land-holding family in Central Scotland...whichever side of the bedclothes you were conceived on. You see, although you may not think it, we have an awful lot in common, Ludovic Fear…or should I call you McBride?"

Fear's eyes stared through MacPherson unseeing and slowly his grip loosened, as his mind struggled to get to grips with The Cyclops' revelation.

Rifling his right hand through his shaggy mop he retreated to the door, shaking his head as if trying to empty it of the words that now kept replaying on a constant loop inside it.

But as he turned to walk out MacPherson spoke again: "What now? What happens with Charlie?"

"That's a question only she can answer…" said Fear stumbling towards the door.

But before he could leave the room The Cyclops spoke again: "You may think you can walk away from me, Mr Fear, but when I have need of you I will call for you, and you will come running."

61

TRUDGING along the track that led towards the broken dyke encircling the chapel graveyard, Fear's mind was in a tailspin.

'How can you be McBride's bastard?' demanded the voice in his head and in truth he found it easier to dismiss the question than try and provide an answer to it.

What mattered here and now was not the past but the present and the future and that meant Monty and...Charlie.

Whatever the game The Cyclops was trying to ensnare him in, the only way he could play it was if he engaged, and gritting his teeth, that was something Fear vowed he would not do.

As he pushed open the rusted gate that led to the graveyard he found himself drawn by an Iona Cross that stood tall and lonely in the shadow of a mighty oak, just a few yards to his left, almost mirroring the desolation and despair he felt now that The Cyclops had injected such uncertainty into his world.

Fear checked the epitaph on it and saw, to his amazement, that it was dedicated to a Dominique MacPherson.

Then he noticed an inscription engraved on the base and hunkering down he found the words of a poem, which he found himself reading aloud:

"Darling these woods have seen ten summers fade
Since thy dear dust in yonder church was laid;
A few more winters, and this heart, the shrine
Of thy fair memory shall be cold as thine.
Yet may some stranger lingering in these ways,
Bestow a tear on grief of other days:
For if he, too, have wept o'er grace and youth
Goodness and wisdom, faith and love and truth,
Untinged with worldly guile or selfish stain,
And ne'er hath looked upon thy like again,
Then, imaged in his sorrow, he may see
All that I loved, and lost, and mourn in thee."

Despite his own problems Fear found himself touched by the melancholy of the words and their sentiments, for now here he was a stranger lingering in these ways and as a moisture trail slipped down his cheek Fear indeed found himself weeping o'er grace and youth...his own...Monty's...he did not know.

Standing up, he took a deep breath, but as he attempted to compose himself the voice of a ten-year-old boy rang out: "Dad, Dad!" shouted Monty and turning, euphoria erupting inside him, Fear saw his son bounding gleefully towards him.

"Monty!" he shouted, scooped his son up in his arms and held him tight.

Standing just a few yards away he saw Charlie smiling his way, and setting his boy down he ruffled his sandy mop, took a step back and looked him up and down. He saw that Monty's complexion was pale and noticed a cut on his left check before he asked: "Are you okay, son? Has Charlie taken good care of you?"

"It was horrible, dad, the flat was covered in blood and that Mr Rothwell lied to me, he said he was a policeman and your pal, dad…how could a bad guy like him be a policeman and a friend of yours?" asked Monty excitedly at a 100mph.

Fear hunkered down and ran an index finger over the small cut, which he noticed had been cleaned, then he took hold of his son's hands: "Because bad men lie, son. But he has gone now and you'll never see him again. You're safe now, son, I promise you," he said and pulled his boy close once again."

Looking over Monty he noticed that Charlie seemed to be hovering a couple of yards away, uncertain whether to intrude on this moment of family joy. Before he could say anything Monty's excited chatter erupted: "Can we show dad the Victorian bathhouse and the waterfall, Charlie? It's well cool!"

After a moment's hesitation Charlie said: "So would dad like to see the bathhouse?" she asked, the use of his son's term of endearment disconcerting Fear as they walked towards her.

"Do I have a choice?" he asked, rolling his eyes.

"It's this way, dad, down the gully, just follow me!" said Monty running ahead.

For a moment their eyes locked and Fear, gesturing back towards the Iona Cross, asked: "It's quite something…is it your…"

"Mother's grave? Yes, it is. Ever since she died, dad has vowed he would restore Lanarkyngs to its former glory and the family plot along with it. But to me, what is the point in restoring a plot of the family who didn't even acknowledge his existence worth…" and her words trailed off into silence.

"But you certainly proved your worth, Charlie. Disposing of Jenkins, driving the crash car and freeing Monty…for a supposed nightclub chanteuse you're some piece of work, Charlie MacPherson!" and as Fear's laughter echoed out loud, he saw the uncertainty in her exquisite features melt.

He reached over and took her hand in his and was met by a smile that warmed his heart.

Ducking under a stray branch, Fear saw a small, square, almost conical roofed building with an intricate pillared archway entrance, looming amongst the fir trees; just in front of it Monty's small figure was jumping up and down and waving towards them.

"Dad, dad, over here, what d'ya think? Cool eh?" his son shouted.

As they carefully picked their way down an earth bank Fear saw that a broken stone bridge, which had almost completely been engulfed in vegetation and reclaimed by Mother Nature, led to the bathhouse.

Although the sound of gurgling water could be heard it remained unseen and as she saw him scanning the surroundings Charlie said: "The old bridge is well hidden now! But it spans the bathing pond that is still either side of it. It's fed by the waterfall you can just make out behind the rhododendron bushes over there to our right. This was my mother's favourite place."

Just as they reached the bottom of the lychee-enveloped bank, Charlie slipped; but before she fell, Fear's powerful grip took hold of her right arm and steadied her. As he did so their bodies came close and their eyes, inches apart, locked.

Despite himself, Fear's right hand seemed to acquire a mind of its own and it reached over and slipped off her black baseball cap, allowing her blonde tresses to cascade free, then his arms encased her and their lips sought each other.

After a lingering moment they parted and walked onto the bridge or, rather, the clumps of grass, moss and other vegetation that made it almost impossible to feel, never mind see, any stone underfoot.

From the entrance to the bathhouse Monty shouted: "Wait until you see the tiles in here, dad, there's a floor under all the leaves; it's well smart."

"Can't wait, son!" replied Fear through a broad smile, but he slowly drew to a stop and took a step up onto what remained of the bridge's right wall. He stared out into the rampant foliage and tried to imagine how magnificent this secret place must have been 100 years or so ago.

Silently Charlie materialised at his right shoulder: "After dad first brought her, if things were troubling mum she would always come back here. It doesn't matter what season it is, it's still a special place, a place of peace…well, apart from the waterfall and the birdsong!" Then after a moment's silence she added: "Mum just loved this spot."

"How long has she been gone?" Fear asked giving her a hand up onto the parapet.

"September 23, 1999," replied Charlie.

"It's amazing that you can hear the water, almost feel it beneath you, but can't see it. Just shows you how quickly nature will reclaim what man neglects. It's almost criminal that a place as beautiful as this once was has been allowed to go to rack and ruin, yet…"

"Yet it is maybe all the more special for it. Mum used to bring me here as a little girl and it was her and dad's dream to recover Lanarkyngs, reclaim it from all this neglect and make it feel loved again."

Her words seemed to spark a shiver of guilt in Fear, and he shot a glance up to the bathhouse where he could see Monty busily scuffing the leaves away from the floor inside with his feet.

"Come on, let's go and see what Rab-haw is up to!" he said, jumping off the wall and holding out a hand for Charlie to take.

As they walked the last few yards towards the broken elegance of the sandstone folly he said: "Your dad asked me what was happening with…us?"

Pulling him close, Charlie stepped onto her tiptoes and kissed him playfully on his cheek: "What do you want to happen with…us!" she teased.